PAPER

and INK

TROPHIES

Painted Wings Publishing

For more information, visit: JHouserWrites.com

Formatting, cover & edge designs by Painted Wings Publishing

Edited by Nia Quinn

ISBNs:

Hardback: 978-1-957334-05-9

Paperback: 978-1-957334-11-0

First Edition: September 2022

10 9 8 7 6 5 4 3 2

FROM THE LIBRARY OF:

_____

How to enjoy your trophy display!

-About Me: 2 pages have been included (in the front & back of this book) to fill with fun tidbits about yourself as the reader. See how much your style & interests have changed after a few hundred books!

-The Great TBR List: 12 pages allow you to easily list 504 books 'To Be Read.'

-The Top Shelf: Decorate with the top 77 books you read & journaled about.

-Journal Pages: 250 pages have been included to rate & review each book you read. Print off a picture of the cover & attach it in the designated spot, or lean on your artistic skills to recreate it!

-The Dusty DNFs (Did Not Finish): Not every book is for every reader. 6 pages are included (72 entries) for you to list the title and your progress before you decided to put the book down (e.g. 100/200 pages read, or 50%). A space is included for commentary.

-Extra Pages: 18 extra lined pages have been added in case those included for other topics didn't happen to be enough for your particular reading habits!

*For best results: use pens, pencils, or markers that are non-bleeding.

**For merch, extra tips, and free templates related to this book journal, go to JHouserWrites.com

About Me

Favorite Genres: _____

Favorite Books/Series: _____

Favorite Authors: _____

Favorite Book Characters: _____

Favorite Tropes: _____

Favorite Covers/Editions: _____

Favorite Places to Read: _____

Bookstore or Library? _____

Bookmark, Dog-ear, or Other? _____

Indie or Traditionally Published Books? _____

Ebook, Paperback, Hardback, or Audio? _____

Cracked or Preserved Spine? _____

My Reading Philosophy: _____

_____

_____

_____

_____

* THE GREAT TBR LIST *

* THE GREAT TBR LIST *

_____   _____

_____   _____

_____   _____

_____   _____

_____   _____

_____   _____

_____   _____

_____   _____

_____   _____

_____   _____

_____   _____

_____   _____

_____   _____

_____   _____

_____   _____

_____   _____

* THE GREAT TBR LIST *

* THE GREAT TBR LIST *

* THE GREAT TBR LIST *

* THE GREAT TBR LIST *

* THE GREAT TBR LIST *

* THE GREAT TBR LIST *

* THE GREAT TBR LIST *

* THE GREAT TBR LIST *

* THE GREAT TBR LIST *

* THE GREAT TBR LIST *

THE TOP SHELF

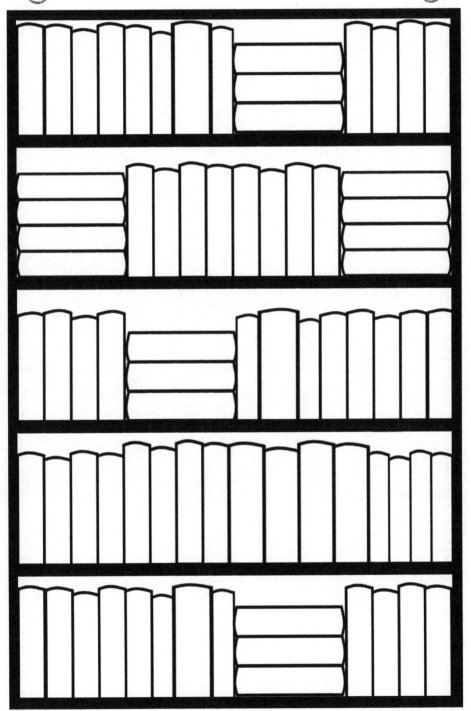

READY.

SET.

READ!

TITLE: _____

GENRE: _____

SERIES: _____

AUTHOR: _____

PAGES: _____

STARTED: _____

FINISHED: _____

☆☆☆☆☆

FORMAT READ: EBOOK / PRINT / AUDIOBOOK

✓ **SYNOPSIS/THINGS I LIKED:**

_____

_____

_____

_____

🚫 **THINGS I DIDN'T LIKE:**

_____

_____

_____

_____

✎ **FAVORITE QUOTE(S):**

_____

_____

_____

_____

_____

_____

_____

_____

1

TITLE: _____

GENRE: _____

SERIES: _____

AUTHOR: _____

PAGES: _____

STARTED: _____

FINISHED: _____

☆ ☆ ☆ ☆ ☆

FORMAT READ: EBOOK / PRINT / AUDIOBOOK

✔ **SYNOPSIS/THINGS I LIKED:**

_____
_____
_____
_____
_____

🚫 **THINGS I DIDN'T LIKE:**

_____
_____
_____
_____

✎ **FAVORITE QUOTE(S):**

_____
_____
_____
_____
_____
_____
_____

✓ SYNOPSIS/THINGS I LIKED:

_____

_____

_____

_____

🚫 THINGS I DIDN'T LIKE:

_____

_____

_____

_____

✎ FAVORITE QUOTE(S):

_____

_____

_____

_____

_____

_____

TITLE: _____

GENRE: _____

SERIES: _____

AUTHOR: _____

PAGES: _____

STARTED: _____

FINISHED: _____

☆ ☆ ☆ ☆ ☆

FORMAT READ: EBOOK / PRINT / AUDIOBOOK   **3**

☑️ **SYNOPSIS/THINGS I LIKED:**

_____
_____
_____
_____

🚫 **THINGS I DIDN'T LIKE:**

_____
_____
_____
_____

📝 **FAVORITE QUOTE(S):**

_____
_____
_____
_____
_____
_____

TITLE: _____

GENRE: _____

SERIES: _____

AUTHOR: _____

PAGES: _____

STARTED: _____

FINISHED: _____

☆ ☆ ☆ ☆ ☆

FORMAT READ: EBOOK / PRINT / AUDIOBOOK

TITLE: _____

GENRE: _____

SERIES: _____

AUTHOR: _____

PAGES: _____

STARTED: _____

FINISHED: _____

☆ ☆ ☆ ☆ ☆

FORMAT READ: EBOOK / PRINT / AUDIOBOOK

✔ SYNOPSIS/THINGS I LIKED:
_____
_____
_____
_____
_____

🚫 THINGS I DIDN'T LIKE:
_____
_____
_____
_____
_____

✒ FAVORITE QUOTE(S):
_____
_____
_____
_____
_____
_____
_____

TITLE: _____

GENRE: _____

SERIES: _____

AUTHOR: _____

PAGES: _____

STARTED: _____

FINISHED: _____

☆ ☆ ☆ ☆ ☆

FORMAT READ: EBOOK / PRINT / AUDIOBOOK

✓ SYNOPSIS/THINGS I LIKED:

_____
_____
_____
_____
_____

🚫 THINGS I DIDN'T LIKE:

_____
_____
_____
_____

✏️ FAVORITE QUOTE(S):

_____
_____
_____
_____
_____
_____
_____

✓ **SYNOPSIS/THINGS I LIKED:**

_____

_____

_____

_____

_____

🚫 **THINGS I DIDN'T LIKE:**

_____

_____

_____

_____

✎ **FAVORITE QUOTE(S):**

_____

_____

_____

_____

_____

_____

TITLE: _____

GENRE: _____

SERIES: _____

AUTHOR: _____

PAGES: _____

STARTED: _____

FINISHED: _____

☆ ☆ ☆ ☆ ☆

FORMAT READ: EBOOK / PRINT / AUDIOBOOK   **7**

✓ SYNOPSIS/THINGS I LIKED:

_____
_____
_____
_____
_____

🚫 THINGS I DIDN'T LIKE:

_____
_____
_____
_____
_____

✎ FAVORITE QUOTE(S):

_____
_____
_____
_____
_____
_____
_____
_____

TITLE: _____

GENRE: _____

SERIES: _____

AUTHOR: _____

PAGES: _____

STARTED: _____

FINISHED: _____

☆ ☆ ☆ ☆ ☆

FORMAT READ: EBOOK / PRINT / AUDIOBOOK

8

TITLE: _____

GENRE: _____

SERIES: _____

AUTHOR: _____

PAGES: _____

STARTED: _____

FINISHED: _____

☆ ☆ ☆ ☆ ☆

FORMAT READ: EBOOK / PRINT / AUDIOBOOK

✔ SYNOPSIS/THINGS I LIKED:

_____
_____
_____
_____
_____

🚫 THINGS I DIDN'T LIKE:

_____
_____
_____
_____
_____

✏️ FAVORITE QUOTE(S):

_____
_____
_____
_____
_____
_____
_____
_____

TITLE: _____

GENRE: _____

SERIES: _____

AUTHOR: _____

PAGES: _____

STARTED: _____

FINISHED: _____

☆☆☆☆☆

FORMAT READ: EBOOK / PRINT / AUDIOBOOK

✓ **SYNOPSIS/THINGS I LIKED:**

_____
_____
_____
_____

🚫 **THINGS I DIDN'T LIKE:**

_____
_____
_____
_____

✎ **FAVORITE QUOTE(S):**

_____
_____
_____
_____
_____
_____

✔ **SYNOPSIS/THINGS I LIKED:**

_____
_____
_____
_____
_____

🚫 **THINGS I DIDN'T LIKE:**

_____
_____
_____
_____
_____

✎ **FAVORITE QUOTE(S):**

_____
_____
_____
_____
_____
_____
_____

TITLE: _____

GENRE: _____

SERIES: _____

AUTHOR: _____

PAGES: _____

STARTED: _____

FINISHED: _____

☆ ☆ ☆ ☆ ☆

✓ **SYNOPSIS/THINGS I LIKED:**

_____

_____

_____

_____

🚫 **THINGS I DIDN'T LIKE:**

_____

_____

_____

_____

📝 **FAVORITE QUOTE(S):**

_____

_____

_____

_____

_____

_____

TITLE: _____

GENRE: _____

SERIES: _____

AUTHOR: _____

PAGES: _____

STARTED: _____

FINISHED: _____

☆ ☆ ☆ ☆ ☆

FORMAT READ: EBOOK / PRINT / AUDIOBOOK

TITLE: _____

GENRE: _____

SERIES: _____

AUTHOR: _____

PAGES: _____

STARTED: _____

FINISHED: _____

☆☆☆☆☆

FORMAT READ: EBOOK / PRINT / AUDIOBOOK

✓ **SYNOPSIS/THINGS I LIKED:**

_____
_____
_____
_____

🚫 **THINGS I DIDN'T LIKE:**

_____
_____
_____
_____

✎ **FAVORITE QUOTE(S):**

_____
_____
_____
_____
_____
_____
_____

TITLE: _____

GENRE: _____

SERIES: _____

AUTHOR: _____

PAGES: _____

STARTED: _____

FINISHED: _____

☆☆☆☆☆

FORMAT READ: EBOOK / PRINT / AUDIOBOOK

✔ **SYNOPSIS/THINGS I LIKED:**

_____
_____
_____
_____
_____

🚫 **THINGS I DIDN'T LIKE:**

_____
_____
_____
_____
_____

✎ **FAVORITE QUOTE(S):**

_____
_____
_____
_____
_____
_____
_____

✓ **SYNOPSIS/THINGS I LIKED:**

_____
_____
_____
_____
_____

🚫 **THINGS I DIDN'T LIKE:**

_____
_____
_____
_____
_____

✏️ **FAVORITE QUOTE(S):**

_____
_____
_____
_____
_____
_____
_____

TITLE: _____

GENRE: _____

SERIES: _____

AUTHOR: _____

PAGES: _____

STARTED: _____

FINISHED: _____

☆ ☆ ☆ ☆ ☆

☑ **SYNOPSIS/THINGS I LIKED:**

_____
_____
_____
_____
_____

🚫 **THINGS I DIDN'T LIKE:**

_____
_____
_____
_____
_____

📝 **FAVORITE QUOTE(S):**

_____
_____
_____
_____
_____
_____
_____

TITLE: _____

GENRE: _____

SERIES: _____

AUTHOR: _____

PAGES: _____

STARTED: _____

FINISHED: _____

☆ ☆ ☆ ☆ ☆

FORMAT READ: EBOOK / PRINT / AUDIOBOOK

TITLE: _____

GENRE: _____

SERIES: _____

AUTHOR: _____

PAGES: _____

STARTED: _____

FINISHED: _____

☆ ☆ ☆ ☆ ☆

FORMAT READ: EBOOK / PRINT / AUDIOBOOK

✓ SYNOPSIS/THINGS I LIKED:

_____
_____
_____
_____
_____

⊘ THINGS I DIDN'T LIKE:

_____
_____
_____
_____
_____

✎ FAVORITE QUOTE(S):

_____
_____
_____
_____
_____
_____
_____

TITLE: _____

GENRE: _____

SERIES: _____

AUTHOR: _____

PAGES: _____

STARTED: _____

FINISHED: _____

☆ ☆ ☆ ☆ ☆

FORMAT READ: EBOOK / PRINT / AUDIOBOOK

☑ **SYNOPSIS/THINGS I LIKED:**

_____
_____
_____
_____

🚫 **THINGS I DIDN'T LIKE:**

_____
_____
_____
_____

✎ **FAVORITE QUOTE(S):**

_____
_____
_____
_____
_____
_____

✓ SYNOPSIS/THINGS I LIKED:

_____
_____
_____
_____
_____

🚫 THINGS I DIDN'T LIKE:

_____
_____
_____
_____
_____

✎ FAVORITE QUOTE(S):

_____
_____
_____
_____
_____
_____
_____

TITLE: _____

GENRE: _____

SERIES: _____

AUTHOR: _____

PAGES: _____

STARTED: _____

FINISHED: _____

☆ ☆ ☆ ☆ ☆

FORMAT READ: EBOOK / PRINT / AUDIOBOOK

☑ **SYNOPSIS/THINGS I LIKED:**

_____
_____
_____
_____
_____

🚫 **THINGS I DIDN'T LIKE:**

_____
_____
_____
_____

✎ **FAVORITE QUOTE(S):**

_____
_____
_____
_____
_____
_____

TITLE: _____

GENRE: _____

SERIES: _____

AUTHOR: _____

PAGES: _____

STARTED: _____

FINISHED: _____

☆ ☆ ☆ ☆ ☆

FORMAT READ: EBOOK / PRINT / AUDIOBOOK

TITLE: _____

GENRE: _____

SERIES: _____

AUTHOR: _____

PAGES: _____

STARTED: _____

FINISHED: _____

☆☆☆☆☆

FORMAT READ: EBOOK / PRINT / AUDIOBOOK

✓ **SYNOPSIS/THINGS I LIKED:**

_____
_____
_____
_____

🚫 **THINGS I DIDN'T LIKE:**

_____
_____
_____
_____

✏️ **FAVORITE QUOTE(S):**

_____
_____
_____
_____
_____
_____

TITLE: _____

GENRE: _____

SERIES: _____

AUTHOR: _____

PAGES: _____

STARTED: _____

FINISHED: _____

☆ ☆ ☆ ☆ ☆

FORMAT READ: EBOOK / PRINT / AUDIOBOOK

✓ SYNOPSIS/THINGS I LIKED:

_____
_____
_____
_____

🚫 THINGS I DIDN'T LIKE:

_____
_____
_____
_____

✎ FAVORITE QUOTE(S):

_____
_____
_____
_____
_____
_____

☑ **SYNOPSIS/THINGS I LIKED:**

_____
_____
_____
_____
_____

🚫 **THINGS I DIDN'T LIKE:**

_____
_____
_____
_____
_____

✏️ **FAVORITE QUOTE(S):**

_____
_____
_____
_____
_____
_____
_____

TITLE: _____

GENRE: _____

SERIES: _____

AUTHOR: _____

PAGES: _____

STARTED: _____

FINISHED: _____

☆ ☆ ☆ ☆ ☆

☑ **SYNOPSIS/THINGS I LIKED:**

_____
_____
_____
_____
_____

🚫 **THINGS I DIDN'T LIKE:**

_____
_____
_____
_____
_____

📝 **FAVORITE QUOTE(S):**

_____
_____
_____
_____
_____
_____
_____

TITLE: _____

GENRE: _____

SERIES: _____

AUTHOR: _____

PAGES: _____

STARTED: _____

FINISHED: _____

☆ ☆ ☆ ☆ ☆

FORMAT READ: EBOOK / PRINT / AUDIOBOOK

TITLE: _____

GENRE: _____

SERIES: _____

AUTHOR: _____

PAGES: _____

STARTED: _____

FINISHED: _____

☆ ☆ ☆ ☆ ☆

FORMAT READ: EBOOK / PRINT / AUDIOBOOK

☑ **SYNOPSIS/THINGS I LIKED:**

_____
_____
_____
_____
_____

🚫 **THINGS I DIDN'T LIKE:**

_____
_____
_____
_____

🖊 **FAVORITE QUOTE(S):**

_____
_____
_____
_____
_____
_____
_____

TITLE: _____

GENRE: _____

SERIES: _____

AUTHOR: _____

PAGES: _____

STARTED: _____

FINISHED: _____

☆☆☆☆☆

FORMAT READ: EBOOK / PRINT / AUDIOBOOK

✓ **SYNOPSIS/THINGS I LIKED:**

_____
_____
_____
_____
_____

🚫 **THINGS I DIDN'T LIKE:**

_____
_____
_____
_____

✎ **FAVORITE QUOTE(S):**

_____
_____
_____
_____
_____
_____
_____

☑ **SYNOPSIS/THINGS I LIKED:**

_____

_____

_____

_____

_____

🚫 **THINGS I DIDN'T LIKE:**

_____

_____

_____

_____

_____

📝 **FAVORITE QUOTE(S):**

_____

_____

_____

_____

_____

_____

_____

TITLE: _____

GENRE: _____

SERIES: _____

AUTHOR: _____

PAGES: _____

STARTED: _____

FINISHED: _____

☆ ☆ ☆ ☆ ☆

FORMAT READ: EBOOK / PRINT / AUDIOBOOK **27**

✓ SYNOPSIS/THINGS I LIKED:

_____
_____
_____
_____
_____

🚫 THINGS I DIDN'T LIKE:

_____
_____
_____
_____
_____

📝 FAVORITE QUOTE(S):

_____
_____
_____
_____
_____
_____
_____

TITLE: _____

GENRE: _____

SERIES: _____

AUTHOR: _____

PAGES: _____

STARTED: _____

FINISHED: _____

☆ ☆ ☆ ☆ ☆

FORMAT READ: EBOOK / PRINT / AUDIOBOOK

TITLE: _____

GENRE: _____

SERIES: _____

AUTHOR: _____

PAGES: _____

STARTED: _____

FINISHED: _____

☆☆☆☆☆

FORMAT READ: EBOOK / PRINT / AUDIOBOOK

✓ SYNOPSIS/THINGS I LIKED:
_____
_____
_____
_____
_____

🚫 THINGS I DIDN'T LIKE:
_____
_____
_____
_____
_____

✎ FAVORITE QUOTE(S):
_____
_____
_____
_____
_____
_____
_____
_____

TITLE: _____

GENRE: _____

SERIES: _____

AUTHOR: _____

PAGES: _____

STARTED: _____

FINISHED: _____

☆☆☆☆☆

FORMAT READ: EBOOK / PRINT / AUDIOBOOK

✓ SYNOPSIS/THINGS I LIKED: _____

_____

_____

_____

_____

🚫 THINGS I DIDN'T LIKE: _____

_____

_____

_____

_____

✎ FAVORITE QUOTE(S): _____

_____

_____

_____

_____

_____

_____

_____

☑ **SYNOPSIS/THINGS I LIKED:**

_____
_____
_____
_____
_____

🚫 **THINGS I DIDN'T LIKE:**

_____
_____
_____
_____

✎ **FAVORITE QUOTE(S):**

_____
_____
_____
_____
_____
_____
_____

TITLE: _____

GENRE: _____

SERIES: _____

AUTHOR: _____

PAGES: _____

STARTED: _____

FINISHED: _____

☆ ☆ ☆ ☆ ☆

FORMAT READ: EBOOK / PRINT / AUDIOBOOK **31**

✔ SYNOPSIS/THINGS I LIKED:

_____
_____
_____
_____
_____

⊘ THINGS I DIDN'T LIKE:

_____
_____
_____
_____
_____

✎ FAVORITE QUOTE(S):

_____
_____
_____
_____
_____
_____
_____

TITLE: _____

GENRE: _____

SERIES: _____

AUTHOR: _____

PAGES: _____

STARTED: _____

FINISHED: _____

☆ ☆ ☆ ☆ ☆

FORMAT READ: EBOOK / PRINT / AUDIOBOOK

TITLE: _____

GENRE: _____

SERIES: _____

AUTHOR: _____

PAGES: _____

STARTED: _____

FINISHED: _____

☆ ☆ ☆ ☆ ☆

FORMAT READ: EBOOK / PRINT / AUDIOBOOK

✔ **SYNOPSIS/THINGS I LIKED:**

_____
_____
_____
_____

🚫 **THINGS I DIDN'T LIKE:**

_____
_____
_____
_____

✏ **FAVORITE QUOTE(S):**

_____
_____
_____
_____
_____
_____

TITLE: _____

GENRE: _____

SERIES: _____

AUTHOR: _____

PAGES: _____

STARTED: _____

FINISHED: _____

☆☆☆☆☆

FORMAT READ: EBOOK / PRINT / AUDIOBOOK

✔ **SYNOPSIS/THINGS I LIKED:**

_____
_____
_____
_____
_____

🚫 **THINGS I DIDN'T LIKE:**

_____
_____
_____
_____

✎ **FAVORITE QUOTE(S):**

_____
_____
_____
_____
_____
_____
_____

✔️ **SYNOPSIS/THINGS I LIKED:**

_____

_____

_____

_____

🚫 **THINGS I DIDN'T LIKE:**

_____

_____

_____

_____

✏️ **FAVORITE QUOTE(S):**

_____

_____

_____

_____

_____

_____

TITLE: _____

GENRE: _____

SERIES: _____

AUTHOR: _____

PAGES: _____

STARTED: _____

FINISHED: _____

☆ ☆ ☆ ☆ ☆

✔ **SYNOPSIS/THINGS I LIKED:**

_____
_____
_____
_____
_____

🚫 **THINGS I DIDN'T LIKE:**

_____
_____
_____
_____
_____

📝 **FAVORITE QUOTE(S):**

_____
_____
_____
_____
_____
_____

TITLE: _____

GENRE: _____

SERIES: _____

AUTHOR: _____

PAGES: _____

STARTED: _____

FINISHED: _____

☆ ☆ ☆ ☆ ☆

FORMAT READ: EBOOK / PRINT / AUDIOBOOK

TITLE: _____

GENRE: _____

SERIES: _____

AUTHOR: _____

PAGES: _____

STARTED: _____

FINISHED: _____

☆☆☆☆☆

FORMAT READ: EBOOK / PRINT / AUDIOBOOK

✓ SYNOPSIS/THINGS I LIKED:

_____
_____
_____
_____
_____

🚫 THINGS I DIDN'T LIKE:

_____
_____
_____
_____

✎ FAVORITE QUOTE(S):

_____
_____
_____
_____
_____
_____
_____

TITLE: _____

GENRE: _____

SERIES: _____

AUTHOR: _____

PAGES: _____

STARTED: _____

FINISHED: _____

☆ ☆ ☆ ☆ ☆

FORMAT READ: EBOOK / PRINT / AUDIOBOOK

SYNOPSIS/THINGS I LIKED:

_____
_____
_____
_____

THINGS I DIDN'T LIKE:

_____
_____
_____
_____

FAVORITE QUOTE(S):

_____
_____
_____
_____
_____
_____
_____

✓ **SYNOPSIS/THINGS I LIKED:**

_____

_____

_____

_____

🚫 **THINGS I DIDN'T LIKE:**

_____

_____

_____

_____

✎ **FAVORITE QUOTE(S):**

_____

_____

_____

_____

_____

_____

TITLE: _____

GENRE: _____

SERIES: _____

AUTHOR: _____

PAGES: _____

STARTED: _____

FINISHED: _____

☆ ☆ ☆ ☆ ☆

FORMAT READ: EBOOK / PRINT / AUDIOBOOK **39**

✓ **SYNOPSIS/THINGS I LIKED:**

_____

_____

_____

_____

_____

🚫 **THINGS I DIDN'T LIKE:**

_____

_____

_____

_____

✏️ **FAVORITE QUOTE(S):**

_____

_____

_____

_____

_____

_____

_____

TITLE: _____

GENRE: _____

SERIES: _____

AUTHOR: _____

PAGES: _____

STARTED: _____

FINISHED: _____

☆ ☆ ☆ ☆ ☆

FORMAT READ: EBOOK / PRINT / AUDIOBOOK

40

TITLE: _____

GENRE: _____

SERIES: _____

AUTHOR: _____

PAGES: _____

STARTED: _____

FINISHED: _____

☆ ☆ ☆ ☆ ☆

FORMAT READ: EBOOK / PRINT / AUDIOBOOK

✓ **SYNOPSIS/THINGS I LIKED:**

_____
_____
_____
_____
_____

🚫 **THINGS I DIDN'T LIKE:**

_____
_____
_____
_____
_____

✏️ **FAVORITE QUOTE(S):**

_____
_____
_____
_____
_____
_____
_____

TITLE: _____

GENRE: _____

SERIES: _____

AUTHOR: _____

PAGES: _____

STARTED: _____

FINISHED: _____

☆ ☆ ☆ ☆ ☆

FORMAT READ: EBOOK / PRINT / AUDIOBOOK

☑ **SYNOPSIS/THINGS I LIKED:**

_____
_____
_____
_____

🚫 **THINGS I DIDN'T LIKE:**

_____
_____
_____
_____

✎ **FAVORITE QUOTE(S):**

_____
_____
_____
_____
_____
_____

✔ **SYNOPSIS/THINGS I LIKED:**

_____
_____
_____
_____
_____

🚫 **THINGS I DIDN'T LIKE:**

_____
_____
_____
_____
_____

📝 **FAVORITE QUOTE(S):**

_____
_____
_____
_____
_____
_____

TITLE: _____

GENRE: _____

SERIES: _____

AUTHOR: _____

PAGES: _____

STARTED: _____

FINISHED: _____

☆ ☆ ☆ ☆ ☆

FORMAT READ: EBOOK / PRINT / AUDIOBOOK 43

✔ **SYNOPSIS/THINGS I LIKED:**

_____

_____

_____

_____

🚫 **THINGS I DIDN'T LIKE:**

_____

_____

_____

_____

✎ **FAVORITE QUOTE(S):**

_____

_____

_____

_____

_____

_____

TITLE: _____

GENRE: _____

SERIES: _____

AUTHOR: _____

PAGES: _____

STARTED: _____

FINISHED: _____

☆ ☆ ☆ ☆ ☆

FORMAT READ: EBOOK / PRINT / AUDIOBOOK

TITLE: _____

GENRE: _____

SERIES: _____

AUTHOR: _____

PAGES: _____

STARTED: _____

FINISHED: _____

☆☆☆☆☆

FORMAT READ: EBOOK / PRINT / AUDIOBOOK

✓ SYNOPSIS/THINGS I LIKED:

_____

_____

_____

_____

🚫 THINGS I DIDN'T LIKE:

_____

_____

_____

_____

✎ FAVORITE QUOTE(S):

_____

_____

_____

_____

_____

_____

_____

TITLE: _____

GENRE: _____

SERIES: _____

AUTHOR: _____

PAGES: _____

STARTED: _____

FINISHED: _____

☆ ☆ ☆ ☆ ☆

FORMAT READ: EBOOK / PRINT / AUDIOBOOK

✅ **SYNOPSIS/THINGS I LIKED:**

_____
_____
_____
_____

🚫 **THINGS I DIDN'T LIKE:**

_____
_____
_____
_____

✏️ **FAVORITE QUOTE(S):**

_____
_____
_____
_____
_____
_____
_____

✔ **SYNOPSIS/THINGS I LIKED:**

_____

_____

_____

_____

_____

🚫 **THINGS I DIDN'T LIKE:**

_____

_____

_____

_____

_____

✏️ **FAVORITE QUOTE(S):**

_____

_____

_____

_____

_____

_____

TITLE: _____

GENRE: _____

SERIES: _____

AUTHOR: _____

PAGES: _____

STARTED: _____

FINISHED: _____

☆ ☆ ☆ ☆ ☆

FORMAT READ: EBOOK / PRINT / AUDIOBOOK **47**

✅ **SYNOPSIS/THINGS I LIKED:**

_____

_____

_____

_____

_____

🚫 **THINGS I DIDN'T LIKE:**

_____

_____

_____

_____

📝 **FAVORITE QUOTE(S):**

_____

_____

_____

_____

_____

_____

TITLE: _____

GENRE: _____

SERIES: _____

AUTHOR: _____

PAGES: _____

STARTED: _____

FINISHED: _____

☆ ☆ ☆ ☆ ☆

FORMAT READ: EBOOK / PRINT / AUDIOBOOK

TITLE: _____

GENRE: _____

SERIES: _____

AUTHOR: _____

PAGES: _____

STARTED: _____

FINISHED: _____

☆☆☆☆☆

FORMAT READ: EBOOK / PRINT / AUDIOBOOK

SYNOPSIS/THINGS I LIKED:

_____
_____
_____
_____

THINGS I DIDN'T LIKE:

_____
_____
_____
_____

FAVORITE QUOTE(S):

_____
_____
_____
_____
_____
_____
_____

49

TITLE: _____

GENRE: _____

SERIES: _____

AUTHOR: _____

PAGES: _____

STARTED: _____

FINISHED: _____

☆ ☆ ☆ ☆ ☆

FORMAT READ: EBOOK / PRINT / AUDIOBOOK

✓ **SYNOPSIS/THINGS I LIKED:**

_____

_____

_____

_____

_____

🚫 **THINGS I DIDN'T LIKE:**

_____

_____

_____

_____

✎ **FAVORITE QUOTE(S):**

_____

_____

_____

_____

_____

_____

_____

✓ SYNOPSIS/THINGS I LIKED:

_____
_____
_____
_____
_____

🚫 THINGS I DIDN'T LIKE:

_____
_____
_____
_____

✎ FAVORITE QUOTE(S):

_____
_____
_____
_____
_____
_____

TITLE: _____

GENRE: _____

SERIES: _____

AUTHOR: _____

PAGES: _____

STARTED: _____

FINISHED: _____

☆ ☆ ☆ ☆ ☆

☑ **SYNOPSIS/THINGS I LIKED:**

_____

_____

_____

_____

🚫 **THINGS I DIDN'T LIKE:**

_____

_____

_____

_____

✎ **FAVORITE QUOTE(S):**

_____

_____

_____

_____

_____

_____

TITLE: _____

GENRE: _____

SERIES: _____

AUTHOR: _____

PAGES: _____

STARTED: _____

FINISHED: _____

☆ ☆ ☆ ☆ ☆

FORMAT READ: EBOOK / PRINT / AUDIOBOOK

TITLE: _____

GENRE: _____

SERIES: _____

AUTHOR: _____

PAGES: _____

STARTED: _____

FINISHED: _____

☆ ☆ ☆ ☆ ☆

FORMAT READ: EBOOK / PRINT / AUDIOBOOK

✓ SYNOPSIS/THINGS I LIKED:
_____
_____
_____
_____
_____

🚫 THINGS I DIDN'T LIKE:
_____
_____
_____
_____
_____

✏️ FAVORITE QUOTE(S):
_____
_____
_____
_____
_____
_____
_____

TITLE: _____

GENRE: _____

SERIES: _____

AUTHOR: _____

PAGES: _____

STARTED: _____

FINISHED: _____

☆☆☆☆☆

FORMAT READ: EBOOK / PRINT / AUDIOBOOK

✓ **SYNOPSIS/THINGS I LIKED:**

_____
_____
_____
_____

🚫 **THINGS I DIDN'T LIKE:**

_____
_____
_____
_____

✎ **FAVORITE QUOTE(S):**

_____
_____
_____
_____
_____
_____
_____

✔ **SYNOPSIS/THINGS I LIKED:**

_____
_____
_____
_____

🚫 **THINGS I DIDN'T LIKE:**

_____
_____
_____
_____

✎ **FAVORITE QUOTE(S):**

_____
_____
_____
_____
_____
_____

TITLE: _____

GENRE: _____

SERIES: _____

AUTHOR: _____

PAGES: _____

STARTED: _____

FINISHED: _____

☆ ☆ ☆ ☆ ☆

✓ Synopsis/Things I liked:

_____

_____

_____

_____

_____

⊘ Things I didn't like:

_____

_____

_____

_____

✎ Favorite quote(s):

_____

_____

_____

_____

_____

_____

Title: _____

Genre: _____

Series: _____

Author: _____

Pages: _____

Started: _____

Finished: _____

☆☆☆☆☆

Format read: Ebook / Print / Audiobook

TITLE: _____

GENRE: _____

SERIES: _____

AUTHOR: _____

PAGES: _____

STARTED: _____

FINISHED: _____

☆☆☆☆☆

FORMAT READ: EBOOK / PRINT / AUDIOBOOK

✓ SYNOPSIS/THINGS I LIKED: _____

_____

_____

_____

_____

🚫 THINGS I DIDN'T LIKE: _____

_____

_____

_____

_____

✎ FAVORITE QUOTE(S): _____

_____

_____

_____

_____

_____

_____

_____

_____

TITLE: _____

GENRE: _____

SERIES: _____

AUTHOR: _____

PAGES: _____

STARTED: _____

FINISHED: _____

☆ ☆ ☆ ☆ ☆

FORMAT READ: EBOOK / PRINT / AUDIOBOOK

✓ **SYNOPSIS/THINGS I LIKED:**

_____
_____
_____
_____

🚫 **THINGS I DIDN'T LIKE:**

_____
_____
_____
_____

✏️ **FAVORITE QUOTE(S):**

_____
_____
_____
_____
_____
_____
_____

✓ SYNOPSIS/THINGS I LIKED:

_____
_____
_____
_____

🚫 THINGS I DIDN'T LIKE:

_____
_____
_____
_____

✏️ FAVORITE QUOTE(S):

_____
_____
_____
_____
_____
_____

TITLE: _____

GENRE: _____

SERIES: _____

AUTHOR: _____

PAGES: _____

STARTED: _____

FINISHED: _____

☆ ☆ ☆ ☆ ☆

✓ **SYNOPSIS/THINGS I LIKED:**

_____
_____
_____
_____
_____

🚫 **THINGS I DIDN'T LIKE:**

_____
_____
_____
_____
_____

✏️ **FAVORITE QUOTE(S):**

_____
_____
_____
_____
_____
_____
_____

TITLE: _____

GENRE: _____

SERIES: _____

AUTHOR: _____

PAGES: _____

STARTED: _____

FINISHED: _____

☆ ☆ ☆ ☆ ☆

FORMAT READ: EBOOK / PRINT / AUDIOBOOK

TITLE: _____

GENRE: _____

SERIES: _____

AUTHOR: _____

PAGES: _____

STARTED: _____

FINISHED: _____

☆ ☆ ☆ ☆ ☆

FORMAT READ: EBOOK / PRINT / AUDIOBOOK

✓ SYNOPSIS/THINGS I LIKED:

_____
_____
_____
_____

🚫 THINGS I DIDN'T LIKE:

_____
_____
_____
_____

✏️ FAVORITE QUOTE(S):

_____
_____
_____
_____
_____
_____
_____
_____

TITLE: _____

GENRE: _____

SERIES: _____

AUTHOR: _____

PAGES: _____

STARTED: _____

FINISHED: _____

☆☆☆☆☆

FORMAT READ: EBOOK / PRINT / AUDIOBOOK

✓ **SYNOPSIS/THINGS I LIKED:**

_____
_____
_____
_____

🚫 **THINGS I DIDN'T LIKE:**

_____
_____
_____
_____

✎ **FAVORITE QUOTE(S):**

_____
_____
_____
_____
_____
_____
_____

✓ **SYNOPSIS/THINGS I LIKED:**

_____
_____
_____
_____
_____

⊘ **THINGS I DIDN'T LIKE:**

_____
_____
_____
_____

✎ **FAVORITE QUOTE(S):**

_____
_____
_____
_____
_____
_____

TITLE: _____

GENRE: _____

SERIES: _____

AUTHOR: _____

PAGES: _____

STARTED: _____

FINISHED: _____

☆ ☆ ☆ ☆ ☆

✅ **SYNOPSIS/THINGS I LIKED:**

_____
_____
_____
_____

🚫 **THINGS I DIDN'T LIKE:**

_____
_____
_____
_____
_____

📝 **FAVORITE QUOTE(S):**

_____
_____
_____
_____
_____
_____

TITLE: _____

GENRE: _____

SERIES: _____

AUTHOR: _____

PAGES: _____

STARTED: _____

FINISHED: _____

☆ ☆ ☆ ☆ ☆

FORMAT READ: EBOOK / PRINT / AUDIOBOOK

TITLE: _____

GENRE: _____

SERIES: _____

AUTHOR: _____

PAGES: _____

STARTED: _____

FINISHED: _____

☆ ☆ ☆ ☆ ☆

FORMAT READ: EBOOK / PRINT / AUDIOBOOK

✔ SYNOPSIS/THINGS I LIKED:

_____
_____
_____
_____

🚫 THINGS I DIDN'T LIKE:

_____
_____
_____
_____

✎ FAVORITE QUOTE(S):

_____
_____
_____
_____
_____
_____

TITLE: _____

GENRE: _____

SERIES: _____

AUTHOR: _____

PAGES: _____

STARTED: _____

FINISHED: _____

☆☆☆☆☆

FORMAT READ: EBOOK / PRINT / AUDIOBOOK

✓ **SYNOPSIS/THINGS I LIKED:**

_____
_____
_____
_____
_____

🚫 **THINGS I DIDN'T LIKE:**

_____
_____
_____
_____
_____

✎ **FAVORITE QUOTE(S):**

_____
_____
_____
_____
_____
_____
_____

✔ **SYNOPSIS/THINGS I LIKED:**

_____
_____
_____
_____
_____

🚫 **THINGS I DIDN'T LIKE:**

_____
_____
_____
_____

📝 **FAVORITE QUOTE(S):**

_____
_____
_____
_____
_____
_____

TITLE: _____

GENRE: _____

SERIES: _____

AUTHOR: _____

PAGES: _____

STARTED: _____

FINISHED: _____

☆ ☆ ☆ ☆ ☆

☑ **Synopsis/Things I liked:**

_____
_____
_____
_____

🚫 **Things I didn't like:**

_____
_____
_____
_____

✎ **Favorite quote(s):**

_____
_____
_____
_____
_____
_____

Title: _____

Genre: _____

Series: _____

Author: _____

Pages: _____

Started: _____

Finished: _____

☆☆☆☆☆

Format read: Ebook / Print / Audiobook

TITLE:

GENRE:

SERIES:

AUTHOR:

PAGES:

STARTED:

FINISHED:

☆☆☆☆☆

FORMAT READ: EBOOK / PRINT / AUDIOBOOK

✓ SYNOPSIS/THINGS I LIKED:

_____
_____
_____
_____
_____

🚫 THINGS I DIDN'T LIKE:

_____
_____
_____
_____

✎ FAVORITE QUOTE(S):

_____
_____
_____
_____
_____
_____
_____
_____

TITLE: _____

GENRE: _____

SERIES: _____

AUTHOR: _____

PAGES: _____

STARTED: _____

FINISHED: _____

☆ ☆ ☆ ☆ ☆

FORMAT READ: EBOOK / PRINT / AUDIOBOOK

✓ **SYNOPSIS/THINGS I LIKED:**

_____
_____
_____
_____
_____

🚫 **THINGS I DIDN'T LIKE:**

_____
_____
_____
_____

✏️ **FAVORITE QUOTE(S):**

_____
_____
_____
_____
_____
_____
_____
_____

✓ **SYNOPSIS/THINGS I LIKED:**

_____
_____
_____
_____

🚫 **THINGS I DIDN'T LIKE:**

_____
_____
_____
_____

✎ **FAVORITE QUOTE(S):**

_____
_____
_____
_____
_____
_____

TITLE: _____

GENRE: _____

SERIES: _____

AUTHOR: _____

PAGES: _____

STARTED: _____

FINISHED: _____

☆ ☆ ☆ ☆ ☆

✅ **SYNOPSIS/THINGS I LIKED:**

_____
_____
_____
_____
_____

🚫 **THINGS I DIDN'T LIKE:**

_____
_____
_____
_____
_____

✏️ **FAVORITE QUOTE(S):**

_____
_____
_____
_____
_____
_____
_____

TITLE: _____

GENRE: _____

SERIES: _____

AUTHOR: _____

PAGES: _____

STARTED: _____

FINISHED: _____

☆ ☆ ☆ ☆ ☆

FORMAT READ: EBOOK / PRINT / AUDIOBOOK

TITLE: _____

GENRE: _____

SERIES: _____

AUTHOR: _____

PAGES: _____

STARTED: _____

FINISHED: _____

☆☆☆☆☆

FORMAT READ: EBOOK / PRINT / AUDIOBOOK

☑ **SYNOPSIS/THINGS I LIKED:**

_____
_____
_____
_____
_____

🚫 **THINGS I DIDN'T LIKE:**

_____
_____
_____
_____

✏️ **FAVORITE QUOTE(S):**

_____
_____
_____
_____
_____
_____
_____

TITLE: _____

GENRE: _____

SERIES: _____

AUTHOR: _____

PAGES: _____

STARTED: _____

FINISHED: _____

☆☆☆☆☆

FORMAT READ: EBOOK / PRINT / AUDIOBOOK

✓ **SYNOPSIS/THINGS I LIKED:**

_____
_____
_____
_____

🚫 **THINGS I DIDN'T LIKE:**

_____
_____
_____
_____

✏️ **FAVORITE QUOTE(S):**

_____
_____
_____
_____
_____
_____
_____

☑ **Synopsis/Things I liked:**

_____

_____

_____

_____

🚫 **Things I didn't like:**

_____

_____

_____

_____

✏️ **Favorite quote(s):**

_____

_____

_____

_____

_____

_____

TITLE: _____

GENRE: _____

SERIES: _____

AUTHOR: _____

PAGES: _____

STARTED: _____

FINISHED: _____

☆ ☆ ☆ ☆ ☆

☑ SYNOPSIS/THINGS I LIKED:

_____
_____
_____
_____
_____

🚫 THINGS I DIDN'T LIKE:

_____
_____
_____
_____
_____

✎ FAVORITE QUOTE(S):

_____
_____
_____
_____
_____
_____

TITLE: _____

GENRE: _____

SERIES: _____

AUTHOR: _____

PAGES: _____

STARTED: _____

FINISHED: _____

☆ ☆ ☆ ☆ ☆

FORMAT READ: EBOOK / PRINT / AUDIOBOOK

76

TITLE: _____

GENRE: _____

SERIES: _____

AUTHOR: _____

PAGES: _____

STARTED: _____

FINISHED: _____

☆ ☆ ☆ ☆ ☆

FORMAT READ: EBOOK / PRINT / AUDIOBOOK

✔ **SYNOPSIS/THINGS I LIKED:**

_____
_____
_____
_____

🚫 **THINGS I DIDN'T LIKE:**

_____
_____
_____
_____

✏️ **FAVORITE QUOTE(S):**

_____
_____
_____
_____
_____
_____
_____

TITLE: _____

GENRE: _____

SERIES: _____

AUTHOR: _____

PAGES: _____

STARTED: _____

FINISHED: _____

☆ ☆ ☆ ☆ ☆

FORMAT READ: EBOOK / PRINT / AUDIOBOOK

☑ **SYNOPSIS/THINGS I LIKED:**

_____
_____
_____
_____

🚫 **THINGS I DIDN'T LIKE:**

_____
_____
_____
_____

✎ **FAVORITE QUOTE(S):**

_____
_____
_____
_____
_____
_____

☑ **SYNOPSIS/THINGS I LIKED:**

_____
_____
_____
_____
_____

🚫 **THINGS I DIDN'T LIKE:**

_____
_____
_____
_____
_____

📝 **FAVORITE QUOTE(S):**

_____
_____
_____
_____
_____
_____
_____

TITLE: _____

GENRE: _____

SERIES: _____

AUTHOR: _____

PAGES: _____

STARTED: _____

FINISHED: _____

☆ ☆ ☆ ☆ ☆

✓ SYNOPSIS/THINGS I LIKED:

_____
_____
_____
_____
_____

🚫 THINGS I DIDN'T LIKE:

_____
_____
_____
_____

✎ FAVORITE QUOTE(S):

_____
_____
_____
_____
_____
_____

TITLE: _____

GENRE: _____

SERIES: _____

AUTHOR: _____

PAGES: _____

STARTED: _____

FINISHED: _____

☆ ☆ ☆ ☆ ☆

FORMAT READ: EBOOK / PRINT / AUDIOBOOK

TITLE: _____

GENRE: _____

SERIES: _____

AUTHOR: _____

PAGES: _____

STARTED: _____

FINISHED: _____

☆ ☆ ☆ ☆ ☆

FORMAT READ: EBOOK / PRINT / AUDIOBOOK

✓ **SYNOPSIS/THINGS I LIKED:**

_____
_____
_____
_____
_____

🚫 **THINGS I DIDN'T LIKE:**

_____
_____
_____
_____

✏️ **FAVORITE QUOTE(S):**

_____
_____
_____
_____
_____
_____
_____

TITLE: _____

GENRE: _____

SERIES: _____

AUTHOR: _____

PAGES: _____

STARTED: _____

FINISHED: _____

☆☆☆☆☆

FORMAT READ: EBOOK / PRINT / AUDIOBOOK

✔ **SYNOPSIS/THINGS I LIKED:**

_____
_____
_____
_____
_____

🚫 **THINGS I DIDN'T LIKE:**

_____
_____
_____
_____
_____

📝 **FAVORITE QUOTE(S):**

_____
_____
_____
_____
_____
_____
_____
_____
_____

✓ SYNOPSIS/THINGS I LIKED:

_____
_____
_____
_____
_____

🚫 THINGS I DIDN'T LIKE:

_____
_____
_____
_____
_____

✏️ FAVORITE QUOTE(S):

_____
_____
_____
_____
_____
_____
_____

TITLE: _____

GENRE: _____

SERIES: _____

AUTHOR: _____

PAGES: _____

STARTED: _____

FINISHED: _____

☆ ☆ ☆ ☆ ☆

FORMAT READ: EBOOK / PRINT / AUDIOBOOK **83**

☑ **SYNOPSIS/THINGS I LIKED:**

_____
_____
_____
_____
_____

🚫 **THINGS I DIDN'T LIKE:**

_____
_____
_____
_____

📝 **FAVORITE QUOTE(S):**

_____
_____
_____
_____
_____
_____

TITLE: _____

GENRE: _____

SERIES: _____

AUTHOR: _____

PAGES: _____

STARTED: _____

FINISHED: _____

☆ ☆ ☆ ☆ ☆

FORMAT READ: EBOOK / PRINT / AUDIOBOOK

Title: _____

Genre: _____

Series: _____

Author: _____

Pages: _____

Started: _____

Finished: _____

☆☆☆☆☆

FORMAT READ: Ebook / Print / Audiobook

✅ **Synopsis/Things I liked:**

_____
_____
_____
_____

🚫 **Things I didn't like:**

_____
_____
_____
_____

📝 **Favorite quote(s):**

_____
_____
_____
_____
_____
_____
_____

TITLE: _____

GENRE: _____

SERIES: _____

AUTHOR: _____

PAGES: _____

STARTED: _____

FINISHED: _____

☆☆☆☆☆

FORMAT READ: EBOOK / PRINT / AUDIOBOOK

✔ SYNOPSIS/THINGS I LIKED:

_____
_____
_____
_____
_____

🚫 THINGS I DIDN'T LIKE:

_____
_____
_____
_____
_____

✎ FAVORITE QUOTE(S):

_____
_____
_____
_____
_____
_____
_____
_____

✓ **SYNOPSIS/THINGS I LIKED:**

_____
_____
_____
_____
_____

🚫 **THINGS I DIDN'T LIKE:**

_____
_____
_____
_____

✏️ **FAVORITE QUOTE(S):**

_____
_____
_____
_____
_____
_____
_____

TITLE: _____

GENRE: _____

SERIES: _____

AUTHOR: _____

PAGES: _____

STARTED: _____

FINISHED: _____

☆ ☆ ☆ ☆ ☆

✔ **SYNOPSIS/THINGS I LIKED:**

_____

_____

_____

_____

🚫 **THINGS I DIDN'T LIKE:**

_____

_____

_____

_____

📝 **FAVORITE QUOTE(S):**

_____

_____

_____

_____

_____

_____

TITLE: _____

GENRE: _____

SERIES: _____

AUTHOR: _____

PAGES: _____

STARTED: _____

FINISHED: _____

☆☆☆☆☆

FORMAT READ: EBOOK / PRINT / AUDIOBOOK

TITLE: _____

GENRE: _____

SERIES: _____

AUTHOR: _____

PAGES: _____

STARTED: _____

FINISHED: _____

☆ ☆ ☆ ☆ ☆

FORMAT READ: EBOOK / PRINT / AUDIOBOOK

✓ **SYNOPSIS/THINGS I LIKED:**

_____
_____
_____
_____
_____

🚫 **THINGS I DIDN'T LIKE:**

_____
_____
_____
_____

✎ **FAVORITE QUOTE(S):**

_____
_____
_____
_____
_____
_____
_____

TITLE: _____

GENRE: _____

SERIES: _____

AUTHOR: _____

PAGES: _____

STARTED: _____

FINISHED: _____

☆☆☆☆☆

FORMAT READ: EBOOK / PRINT / AUDIOBOOK

✓ SYNOPSIS/THINGS I LIKED:

_____
_____
_____
_____
_____

🚫 THINGS I DIDN'T LIKE:

_____
_____
_____
_____
_____

✏️ FAVORITE QUOTE(S):

_____
_____
_____
_____
_____
_____
_____
_____

✓ **SYNOPSIS/THINGS I LIKED:**

_____
_____
_____
_____
_____

🚫 **THINGS I DIDN'T LIKE:**

_____
_____
_____
_____
_____

✎ **FAVORITE QUOTE(S):**

_____
_____
_____
_____
_____
_____
_____

TITLE: _____

GENRE: _____

SERIES: _____

AUTHOR: _____

PAGES: _____

STARTED: _____

FINISHED: _____

☆ ☆ ☆ ☆ ☆

✔ **SYNOPSIS/THINGS I LIKED:**

_____
_____
_____
_____

🚫 **THINGS I DIDN'T LIKE:**

_____
_____
_____
_____

📝 **FAVORITE QUOTE(S):**

_____
_____
_____
_____
_____
_____

TITLE: _____

GENRE: _____

SERIES: _____

AUTHOR: _____

PAGES: _____

STARTED: _____

FINISHED: _____

☆ ☆ ☆ ☆ ☆

FORMAT READ: EBOOK / PRINT / AUDIOBOOK

TITLE: _____

GENRE: _____

SERIES: _____

AUTHOR: _____

PAGES: _____

STARTED: _____

FINISHED: _____

☆ ☆ ☆ ☆ ☆

FORMAT READ: EBOOK / PRINT / AUDIOBOOK

☑ **SYNOPSIS/THINGS I LIKED:**

_____
_____
_____
_____

🚫 **THINGS I DIDN'T LIKE:**

_____
_____
_____
_____

✎ **FAVORITE QUOTE(S):**

_____
_____
_____
_____
_____
_____
_____

TITLE: _____

GENRE: _____

SERIES: _____

AUTHOR: _____

PAGES: _____

STARTED: _____

FINISHED: _____

☆☆☆☆☆

FORMAT READ: EBOOK / PRINT / AUDIOBOOK

✓ **SYNOPSIS/THINGS I LIKED:**

_____
_____
_____
_____

🚫 **THINGS I DIDN'T LIKE:**

_____
_____
_____
_____

📝 **FAVORITE QUOTE(S):**

_____
_____
_____
_____
_____
_____
_____

✔ **SYNOPSIS/THINGS I LIKED:**

_____
_____
_____
_____

🚫 **THINGS I DIDN'T LIKE:**

_____
_____
_____
_____

📝 **FAVORITE QUOTE(S):**

_____
_____
_____
_____
_____
_____

TITLE: _____

GENRE: _____

SERIES: _____

AUTHOR: _____

PAGES: _____

STARTED: _____

FINISHED: _____

☆☆☆☆☆

✓ SYNOPSIS/THINGS I LIKED:

_____

_____

_____

_____

🚫 THINGS I DIDN'T LIKE:

_____

_____

_____

_____

✏️ FAVORITE QUOTE(S):

_____

_____

_____

_____

_____

_____

_____

TITLE: _____

GENRE: _____

SERIES: _____

AUTHOR: _____

PAGES: _____

STARTED: _____

FINISHED: _____

☆ ☆ ☆ ☆ ☆

FORMAT READ: EBOOK / PRINT / AUDIOBOOK

TITLE: _____

GENRE: _____

SERIES: _____

AUTHOR: _____

PAGES: _____

STARTED: _____

FINISHED: _____

☆☆☆☆☆

FORMAT READ: EBOOK / PRINT / AUDIOBOOK

✓ SYNOPSIS/THINGS I LIKED:

_____
_____
_____
_____

🚫 THINGS I DIDN'T LIKE:

_____
_____
_____
_____

📝 FAVORITE QUOTE(S):

_____
_____
_____
_____
_____
_____
_____

TITLE: _____

GENRE: _____

SERIES: _____

AUTHOR: _____

PAGES: _____

STARTED: _____

FINISHED: _____

☆☆☆☆☆

FORMAT READ: EBOOK / PRINT / AUDIOBOOK

✓ **SYNOPSIS/THINGS I LIKED:**

_____
_____
_____
_____

🚫 **THINGS I DIDN'T LIKE:**

_____
_____
_____
_____

✎ **FAVORITE QUOTE(S):**

_____
_____
_____
_____
_____
_____

✓ **SYNOPSIS/THINGS I LIKED:**

_____

_____

_____

_____

🚫 **THINGS I DIDN'T LIKE:**

_____

_____

_____

_____

✎ **FAVORITE QUOTE(S):**

_____

_____

_____

_____

_____

_____

TITLE: _____

GENRE: _____

SERIES: _____

AUTHOR: _____

PAGES: _____

STARTED: _____

FINISHED: _____

☆ ☆ ☆ ☆ ☆

☑ **SYNOPSIS/THINGS I LIKED:**

_____
_____
_____
_____

🚫 **THINGS I DIDN'T LIKE:**

_____
_____
_____
_____

📝 **FAVORITE QUOTE(S):**

_____
_____
_____
_____
_____
_____
_____

TITLE: _____

GENRE: _____

SERIES: _____

AUTHOR: _____

PAGES: _____

STARTED: _____

FINISHED: _____

☆ ☆ ☆ ☆ ☆

FORMAT READ: EBOOK / PRINT / AUDIOBOOK

TITLE: _____

GENRE: _____

SERIES: _____

AUTHOR: _____

PAGES: _____

STARTED: _____

FINISHED: _____

☆ ☆ ☆ ☆ ☆

FORMAT READ: EBOOK / PRINT / AUDIOBOOK

✓ **SYNOPSIS/THINGS I LIKED:**

_____
_____
_____
_____
_____

🚫 **THINGS I DIDN'T LIKE:**

_____
_____
_____
_____

✎ **FAVORITE QUOTE(S):**

_____
_____
_____
_____
_____
_____
_____

TITLE: _____

GENRE: _____

SERIES: _____

AUTHOR: _____

PAGES: _____

STARTED: _____

FINISHED: _____

☆ ☆ ☆ ☆ ☆

FORMAT READ: EBOOK / PRINT / AUDIOBOOK

✓ **SYNOPSIS/THINGS I LIKED:**

_____
_____
_____
_____

🚫 **THINGS I DIDN'T LIKE:**

_____
_____
_____
_____

✏️ **FAVORITE QUOTE(S):**

_____
_____
_____
_____
_____
_____

☑ **Synopsis/Things I liked:**

_____
_____
_____
_____
_____

🚫 **Things I didn't like:**

_____
_____
_____
_____
_____

📝 **Favorite quote(s):**

_____
_____
_____
_____
_____
_____
_____
_____

Title: _____

Genre: _____

Series: _____

Author: _____

Pages: _____

Started: _____

Finished: _____

☆ ☆ ☆ ☆ ☆

FORMAT READ: EBOOK / PRINT / AUDIOBOOK

☑ **Synopsis/Things I liked:**

_____
_____
_____
_____
_____

🚫 **Things I didn't like:**

_____
_____
_____
_____

📝 **Favorite quote(s):**

_____
_____
_____
_____
_____
_____
_____

Title: _____

Genre: _____

Series: _____

Author: _____

Pages: _____

Started: _____

Finished: _____

★ ★ ★ ★ ☆

Format read: Ebook / Print / Audiobook

TITLE: _____

GENRE: _____

SERIES: _____

AUTHOR: _____

PAGES: _____

STARTED: _____

FINISHED: _____

☆ ☆ ☆ ☆ ☆

FORMAT READ: EBOOK / PRINT / AUDIOBOOK

☑ **SYNOPSIS/THINGS I LIKED:**

_____
_____
_____
_____

🚫 **THINGS I DIDN'T LIKE:**

_____
_____
_____
_____

✏️ **FAVORITE QUOTE(S):**

_____
_____
_____
_____
_____
_____
_____

TITLE: _____

GENRE: _____

SERIES: _____

AUTHOR: _____

PAGES: _____

STARTED: _____

FINISHED: _____

☆☆☆☆☆

FORMAT READ: EBOOK / PRINT / AUDIOBOOK

✓ **SYNOPSIS/THINGS I LIKED:**

_____
_____
_____
_____

🚫 **THINGS I DIDN'T LIKE:**

_____
_____
_____
_____

✏️ **FAVORITE QUOTE(S):**

_____
_____
_____
_____
_____
_____
_____

☑ **Synopsis/Things I liked:**

_____
_____
_____
_____
_____

🚫 **Things I didn't like:**

_____
_____
_____
_____

📝 **Favorite quote(s):**

_____
_____
_____
_____
_____
_____

Title: _____

Genre: _____

Series: _____

Author: _____

Pages: _____

Started: _____

Finished: _____

☆ ☆ ☆ ☆ ☆

Format read: Ebook / Print / Audiobook

✔ **Synopsis/Things I liked:**

_____

_____

_____

_____

🚫 **Things I didn't like:**

_____

_____

_____

_____

📝 **Favorite quote(s):**

_____

_____

_____

_____

_____

_____

Title: _____

Genre: _____

Series: _____

Author: _____

Pages: _____

Started: _____

Finished: _____

☆ ☆ ☆ ☆ ☆

Format read: Ebook / Print / Audiobook

TITLE: _____

GENRE: _____

SERIES: _____

AUTHOR: _____

PAGES: _____

STARTED: _____

FINISHED: _____

☆ ☆ ☆ ☆ ☆

FORMAT READ: EBOOK / PRINT / AUDIOBOOK

✓ SYNOPSIS/THINGS I LIKED:

_____
_____
_____
_____
_____

🚫 THINGS I DIDN'T LIKE:

_____
_____
_____
_____

✎ FAVORITE QUOTE(S):

_____
_____
_____
_____
_____
_____
_____

TITLE: _____

GENRE: _____

SERIES: _____

AUTHOR: _____

PAGES: _____

STARTED: _____

FINISHED: _____

☆☆☆☆☆

FORMAT READ: EBOOK / PRINT / AUDIOBOOK

☑ **SYNOPSIS/THINGS I LIKED:**

_____
_____
_____
_____

🚫 **THINGS I DIDN'T LIKE:**

_____
_____
_____
_____

✎ **FAVORITE QUOTE(S):**

_____
_____
_____
_____
_____
_____

☑ **SYNOPSIS/THINGS I LIKED:**

_____
_____
_____
_____
_____

🚫 **THINGS I DIDN'T LIKE:**

_____
_____
_____
_____

✎ **FAVORITE QUOTE(S):**

_____
_____
_____
_____
_____
_____
_____

TITLE: _____

GENRE: _____

SERIES: _____

AUTHOR: _____

PAGES: _____

STARTED: _____

FINISHED: _____

☆ ☆ ☆ ☆ ☆

FORMAT READ: EBOOK / PRINT / AUDIOBOOK

☑ Synopsis/Things I liked:

_____
_____
_____
_____
_____

🚫 Things I didn't like:

_____
_____
_____
_____

✏ Favorite quote(s):

_____
_____
_____
_____
_____
_____
_____

Title: _____

Genre: _____

Series: _____

Author: _____

Pages: _____

Started: _____

Finished: _____

☆ ☆ ☆ ☆ ☆

Format read: Ebook / Print / Audiobook

TITLE: _____

GENRE: _____

SERIES: _____

AUTHOR: _____

PAGES: _____

STARTED: _____

FINISHED: _____

☆ ☆ ☆ ☆ ☆

FORMAT READ: EBOOK / PRINT / AUDIOBOOK

✓ **SYNOPSIS/THINGS I LIKED:**

_____
_____
_____
_____

⊘ **THINGS I DIDN'T LIKE:**

_____
_____
_____
_____

✎ **FAVORITE QUOTE(S):**

_____
_____
_____
_____
_____
_____
_____

TITLE: _____

GENRE: _____

SERIES: _____

AUTHOR: _____

PAGES: _____

STARTED: _____

FINISHED: _____

☆☆☆☆☆

FORMAT READ: EBOOK / PRINT / AUDIOBOOK

✔ **SYNOPSIS/THINGS I LIKED:**

_____
_____
_____
_____

🚫 **THINGS I DIDN'T LIKE:**

_____
_____
_____
_____

✎ **FAVORITE QUOTE(S):**

_____
_____
_____
_____
_____
_____

_____
_____
_____
_____
_____

🚫 THINGS I DIDN'T LIKE:

_____
_____
_____
_____
_____

✎ FAVORITE QUOTE(S):

_____
_____
_____
_____
_____
_____
_____

TITLE: _____

GENRE: _____

SERIES: _____

AUTHOR: _____

PAGES: _____

STARTED: _____

FINISHED: _____

☆ ☆ ☆ ☆ ☆

FORMAT READ: EBOOK / PRINT / AUDIOBOOK

✔ **SYNOPSIS/THINGS I LIKED:**

_____

_____

_____

_____

_____

🚫 **THINGS I DIDN'T LIKE:**

_____

_____

_____

_____

📝 **FAVORITE QUOTE(S):**

_____

_____

_____

_____

_____

_____

TITLE: _____

GENRE: _____

SERIES: _____

AUTHOR: _____

PAGES: _____

STARTED: _____

FINISHED: _____

☆ ☆ ☆ ☆ ☆

FORMAT READ: EBOOK / PRINT / AUDIOBOOK

TITLE: _____

GENRE: _____

SERIES: _____

AUTHOR: _____

PAGES: _____

STARTED: _____

FINISHED: _____

☆ ☆ ☆ ☆ ☆

FORMAT READ: EBOOK / PRINT / AUDIOBOOK

✔ SYNOPSIS/THINGS I LIKED:
_____
_____
_____
_____
_____

🚫 THINGS I DIDN'T LIKE:
_____
_____
_____
_____

✎ FAVORITE QUOTE(S):
_____
_____
_____
_____
_____
_____
_____

TITLE: _____

GENRE: _____

SERIES: _____

AUTHOR: _____

PAGES: _____

STARTED: _____

FINISHED: _____

☆☆☆☆☆

FORMAT READ: EBOOK / PRINT / AUDIOBOOK

☑ **SYNOPSIS/THINGS I LIKED:**

_____
_____
_____
_____
_____

🚫 **THINGS I DIDN'T LIKE:**

_____
_____
_____
_____

✎ **FAVORITE QUOTE(S):**

_____
_____
_____
_____
_____
_____
_____

✓ **SYNOPSIS/THINGS I LIKED:**

_____

_____

_____

_____

🚫 **THINGS I DIDN'T LIKE:**

_____

_____

_____

_____

📝 **FAVORITE QUOTE(S):**

_____

_____

_____

_____

_____

_____

TITLE: _____

GENRE: _____

SERIES: _____

AUTHOR: _____

PAGES: _____

STARTED: _____

FINISHED: _____

☆ ☆ ☆ ☆ ☆

FORMAT READ: EBOOK / PRINT / AUDIOBOOK

☑ **SYNOPSIS/THINGS I LIKED:**

_____
_____
_____
_____
_____

🚫 **THINGS I DIDN'T LIKE:**

_____
_____
_____
_____
_____

✎ **FAVORITE QUOTE(S):**

_____
_____
_____
_____
_____
_____
_____

TITLE: _____

GENRE: _____

SERIES: _____

AUTHOR: _____

PAGES: _____

STARTED: _____

FINISHED: _____

☆ ☆ ☆ ☆ ☆

FORMAT READ: EBOOK / PRINT / AUDIOBOOK

TITLE: _____

GENRE: _____

SERIES: _____

AUTHOR: _____

PAGES: _____

STARTED: _____

FINISHED: _____

☆☆☆☆☆

FORMAT READ: EBOOK / PRINT / AUDIOBOOK

☑ **SYNOPSIS/THINGS I LIKED:**

_____
_____
_____
_____
_____

🚫 **THINGS I DIDN'T LIKE:**

_____
_____
_____
_____
_____

✎ **FAVORITE QUOTE(S):**

_____
_____
_____
_____
_____
_____
_____
_____

TITLE: _____

GENRE: _____

SERIES: _____

AUTHOR: _____

PAGES: _____

STARTED: _____

FINISHED: _____

☆☆☆☆☆

FORMAT READ: EBOOK / PRINT / AUDIOBOOK

✓ **SYNOPSIS/THINGS I LIKED:**

_____
_____
_____
_____

🚫 **THINGS I DIDN'T LIKE:**

_____
_____
_____
_____

✎ **FAVORITE QUOTE(S):**

_____
_____
_____
_____
_____
_____
_____
_____

✓ **SYNOPSIS/THINGS I LIKED:**

_____
_____
_____
_____
_____

🚫 **THINGS I DIDN'T LIKE:**

_____
_____
_____
_____

✎ **FAVORITE QUOTE(S):**

_____
_____
_____
_____
_____
_____
_____

TITLE: _____

GENRE: _____

SERIES: _____

AUTHOR: _____

PAGES: _____

STARTED: _____

FINISHED: _____

☆ ☆ ☆ ☆ ☆

FORMAT READ: EBOOK / PRINT / AUDIOBOOK

☑ **Synopsis/Things I liked:**

_____
_____
_____
_____
_____

🚫 **Things I didn't like:**

_____
_____
_____
_____
_____

📝 **Favorite quote(s):**

_____
_____
_____
_____
_____
_____
_____

Title: _____

Genre: _____

Series: _____

Author: _____

Pages: _____

Started: _____

Finished: _____

☆ ☆ ☆ ☆ ☆

Format read: Ebook / Print / Audiobook

TITLE: _____

GENRE: _____

SERIES: _____

AUTHOR: _____

PAGES: _____

STARTED: _____

FINISHED: _____

☆ ☆ ☆ ☆ ☆

FORMAT READ: EBOOK / PRINT / AUDIOBOOK

✅ **SYNOPSIS/THINGS I LIKED:**

_____
_____
_____
_____
_____

🚫 **THINGS I DIDN'T LIKE:**

_____
_____
_____
_____
_____

✏️ **FAVORITE QUOTE(S):**

_____
_____
_____
_____
_____
_____
_____
_____

125

TITLE: _____

GENRE: _____

SERIES: _____

AUTHOR: _____

PAGES: _____

STARTED: _____

FINISHED: _____

☆ ☆ ☆ ☆ ☆

FORMAT READ: EBOOK / PRINT / AUDIOBOOK

✓ **SYNOPSIS/THINGS I LIKED:**

_____

_____

_____

_____

🚫 **THINGS I DIDN'T LIKE:**

_____

_____

_____

_____

✎ **FAVORITE QUOTE(S):**

_____

_____

_____

_____

_____

_____

_____

✓ **SYNOPSIS/THINGS I LIKED:**

_____
_____
_____
_____
_____

🚫 **THINGS I DIDN'T LIKE:**

_____
_____
_____
_____

✎ **FAVORITE QUOTE(S):**

_____
_____
_____
_____
_____
_____

TITLE: _____

GENRE: _____

SERIES: _____

AUTHOR: _____

PAGES: _____

STARTED: _____

FINISHED: _____

☆ ☆ ☆ ☆ ☆

FORMAT READ: EBOOK / PRINT / AUDIOBOOK

☑ **Synopsis/Things I liked:**

_____
_____
_____
_____

🚫 **Things I didn't like:**

_____
_____
_____
_____

✏️ **Favorite quote(s):**

_____
_____
_____
_____
_____
_____
_____

Title: _____

Genre: _____

Series: _____

Author: _____

Pages: _____

Started: _____

Finished: _____

☆ ☆ ☆ ☆ ☆

Format read: Ebook / Print / Audiobook

TITLE: _____

GENRE: _____

SERIES: _____

AUTHOR: _____

PAGES: _____

STARTED: _____

FINISHED: _____

☆ ☆ ☆ ☆ ☆

FORMAT READ: EBOOK / PRINT / AUDIOBOOK

✔ SYNOPSIS/THINGS I LIKED:

_____
_____
_____
_____
_____

🚫 THINGS I DIDN'T LIKE:

_____
_____
_____
_____
_____

✎ FAVORITE QUOTE(S):

_____
_____
_____
_____
_____
_____
_____

TITLE: _____

GENRE: _____

SERIES: _____

AUTHOR: _____

PAGES: _____

STARTED: _____

FINISHED: _____

☆☆☆☆☆

FORMAT READ: EBOOK / PRINT / AUDIOBOOK

✅ **SYNOPSIS/THINGS I LIKED:**

_____
_____
_____
_____

🚫 **THINGS I DIDN'T LIKE:**

_____
_____
_____
_____

✏️ **FAVORITE QUOTE(S):**

_____
_____
_____
_____
_____
_____
_____

☑ **SYNOPSIS/THINGS I LIKED:**

_____
_____
_____
_____
_____

🚫 **THINGS I DIDN'T LIKE:**

_____
_____
_____
_____
_____

📝 **FAVORITE QUOTE(S):**

_____
_____
_____
_____
_____
_____
_____

TITLE: _____

GENRE: _____

SERIES: _____

AUTHOR: _____

PAGES: _____

STARTED: _____

FINISHED: _____

☆☆☆☆☆

FORMAT READ: EBOOK / PRINT / AUDIOBOOK

✓ SYNOPSIS/THINGS I LIKED:

_____

_____

_____

_____

🚫 THINGS I DIDN'T LIKE:

_____

_____

_____

_____

✎ FAVORITE QUOTE(S):

_____

_____

_____

_____

_____

_____

_____

TITLE: _____

GENRE: _____

SERIES: _____

AUTHOR: _____

PAGES: _____

STARTED: _____

FINISHED: _____

☆ ☆ ☆ ☆ ☆

FORMAT READ: EBOOK / PRINT / AUDIOBOOK

TITLE: _____

GENRE: _____

SERIES: _____

AUTHOR: _____

PAGES: _____

STARTED: _____

FINISHED: _____

☆☆☆☆☆

FORMAT READ: EBOOK / PRINT / AUDIOBOOK

✔ **SYNOPSIS/THINGS I LIKED:**

_____
_____
_____
_____

🚫 **THINGS I DIDN'T LIKE:**

_____
_____
_____
_____

📝 **FAVORITE QUOTE(S):**

_____
_____
_____
_____
_____
_____
_____

TITLE: _____

GENRE: _____

SERIES: _____

AUTHOR: _____

PAGES: _____

STARTED: _____

FINISHED: _____

☆☆☆☆☆

FORMAT READ: EBOOK / PRINT / AUDIOBOOK

✔ **SYNOPSIS/THINGS I LIKED:**

_____

_____

_____

_____

🚫 **THINGS I DIDN'T LIKE:**

_____

_____

_____

_____

✎ **FAVORITE QUOTE(S):**

_____

_____

_____

_____

_____

_____

✓ **Synopsis/Things I liked:**

_____
_____
_____
_____
_____

🚫 **Things I didn't like:**

_____
_____
_____
_____

✎ **Favorite quote(s):**

_____
_____
_____
_____
_____
_____

Title: _____

Genre: _____

Series: _____

Author: _____

Pages: _____

Started: _____

Finished: _____

☆ ☆ ☆ ☆ ☆

Format read: Ebook / Print / Audiobook

135

✅ **SYNOPSIS/THINGS I LIKED:**

_____
_____
_____
_____
_____

🚫 **THINGS I DIDN'T LIKE:**

_____
_____
_____
_____
_____

📝 **FAVORITE QUOTE(S):**

_____
_____
_____
_____
_____
_____
_____

TITLE: _____

GENRE: _____

SERIES: _____

AUTHOR: _____

PAGES: _____

STARTED: _____

FINISHED: _____

☆ ☆ ☆ ☆ ☆

FORMAT READ: EBOOK / PRINT / AUDIOBOOK

Title: _____

Genre: _____

Series: _____

Author: _____

Pages: _____

Started: _____

Finished: _____

☆ ☆ ☆ ☆ ☆

Format read: Ebook / Print / Audiobook

☑ **Synopsis/Things I liked:**

_____
_____
_____
_____

🚫 **Things I didn't like:**

_____
_____
_____
_____

🖊 **Favorite quote(s):**

_____
_____
_____
_____
_____
_____
_____

TITLE: _____

GENRE: _____

SERIES: _____

AUTHOR: _____

PAGES: _____

STARTED: _____

FINISHED: _____

☆☆☆☆☆

FORMAT READ: EBOOK / PRINT / AUDIOBOOK

✓ **SYNOPSIS/THINGS I LIKED:**

_____
_____
_____
_____

🚫 **THINGS I DIDN'T LIKE:**

_____
_____
_____
_____

✏️ **FAVORITE QUOTE(S):**

_____
_____
_____
_____
_____
_____

✓ SYNOPSIS/THINGS I LIKED:

_____

_____

_____

_____

🚫 THINGS I DIDN'T LIKE:

_____

_____

_____

_____

📝 FAVORITE QUOTE(S):

_____

_____

_____

_____

_____

_____

TITLE: _____

GENRE: _____

SERIES: _____

AUTHOR: _____

PAGES: _____

STARTED: _____

FINISHED: _____

☆ ☆ ☆ ☆ ☆

FORMAT READ: EBOOK / PRINT / AUDIOBOOK

☑ **SYNOPSIS/THINGS I LIKED:**

_____

_____

_____

_____

_____

🚫 **THINGS I DIDN'T LIKE:**

_____

_____

_____

_____

_____

📝 **FAVORITE QUOTE(S):**

_____

_____

_____

_____

_____

_____

_____

TITLE: _____

GENRE: _____

SERIES: _____

AUTHOR: _____

PAGES: _____

STARTED: _____

FINISHED: _____

☆ ☆ ☆ ☆ ☆

FORMAT READ: EBOOK / PRINT / AUDIOBOOK

TITLE: _____

GENRE: _____

SERIES: _____

AUTHOR: _____

PAGES: _____

STARTED: _____

FINISHED: _____

☆ ☆ ☆ ☆ ☆

FORMAT READ: EBOOK / PRINT / AUDIOBOOK

☑ SYNOPSIS/THINGS I LIKED:

_____
_____
_____
_____
_____

🚫 THINGS I DIDN'T LIKE:

_____
_____
_____
_____
_____

✎ FAVORITE QUOTE(S):

_____
_____
_____
_____
_____
_____
_____

TITLE: _____

GENRE: _____

SERIES: _____

AUTHOR: _____

PAGES: _____

STARTED: _____

FINISHED: _____

☆☆☆☆☆

FORMAT READ: EBOOK / PRINT / AUDIOBOOK

✓ **SYNOPSIS/THINGS I LIKED:**

_____
_____
_____
_____
_____

🚫 **THINGS I DIDN'T LIKE:**

_____
_____
_____
_____
_____

📝 **FAVORITE QUOTE(S):**

_____
_____
_____
_____
_____
_____
_____
_____

✓ **SYNOPSIS/THINGS I LIKED:**

_____
_____
_____
_____
_____

🚫 **THINGS I DIDN'T LIKE:**

_____
_____
_____
_____
_____

📝 **FAVORITE QUOTE(S):**

_____
_____
_____
_____
_____
_____
_____

TITLE: _____

GENRE: _____

SERIES: _____

AUTHOR: _____

PAGES: _____

STARTED: _____

FINISHED: _____

☆ ☆ ☆ ☆ ☆

FORMAT READ: EBOOK / PRINT / AUDIOBOOK

☑ SYNOPSIS/THINGS I LIKED:

_____

_____

_____

_____

🚫 THINGS I DIDN'T LIKE:

_____

_____

_____

_____

📝 FAVORITE QUOTE(S):

_____

_____

_____

_____

_____

_____

_____

TITLE: _____

GENRE: _____

SERIES: _____

AUTHOR: _____

PAGES: _____

STARTED: _____

FINISHED: _____

☆☆☆☆☆

FORMAT READ: EBOOK / PRINT / AUDIOBOOK

144

TITLE: _____

GENRE: _____

SERIES: _____

AUTHOR: _____

PAGES: _____

STARTED: _____

FINISHED: _____

☆ ☆ ☆ ☆ ☆

FORMAT READ: EBOOK / PRINT / AUDIOBOOK

✓ **SYNOPSIS/THINGS I LIKED:**

_____
_____
_____
_____

🚫 **THINGS I DIDN'T LIKE:**

_____
_____
_____
_____

📝 **FAVORITE QUOTE(S):**

_____
_____
_____
_____
_____
_____
_____

TITLE: _____

GENRE: _____

SERIES: _____

AUTHOR: _____

PAGES: _____

STARTED: _____

FINISHED: _____

☆☆☆☆☆

FORMAT READ: EBOOK / PRINT / AUDIOBOOK

☑ SYNOPSIS/THINGS I LIKED:

_____
_____
_____
_____

🚫 THINGS I DIDN'T LIKE:

_____
_____
_____
_____

🖉 FAVORITE QUOTE(S):

_____
_____
_____
_____
_____
_____
_____
_____

☑ **Synopsis/Things I liked:**

_____
_____
_____
_____

⊘ **Things I didn't like:**

_____
_____
_____
_____

✎ **Favorite quote(s):**

_____
_____
_____
_____
_____
_____

Title: _____

Genre: _____

Series: _____

Author: _____

Pages: _____

Started: _____

Finished: _____

☆ ☆ ☆ ☆ ☆

Format read: Ebook / Print / Audiobook

✔ SYNOPSIS/THINGS I LIKED:

_____
_____
_____
_____
_____

🚫 THINGS I DIDN'T LIKE:

_____
_____
_____
_____
_____

✎ FAVORITE QUOTE(S):

_____
_____
_____
_____
_____
_____
_____

TITLE: _____

GENRE: _____

SERIES: _____

AUTHOR: _____

PAGES: _____

STARTED: _____

FINISHED: _____

☆ ☆ ☆ ☆ ☆

FORMAT READ: EBOOK / PRINT / AUDIOBOOK

TITLE: _____

GENRE: _____

SERIES: _____

AUTHOR: _____

PAGES: _____

STARTED: _____

FINISHED: _____

☆ ☆ ☆ ☆ ☆

FORMAT READ: EBOOK / PRINT / AUDIOBOOK

☑ SYNOPSIS/THINGS I LIKED:

_____

_____

_____

_____

⊘ THINGS I DIDN'T LIKE:

_____

_____

_____

_____

✎ FAVORITE QUOTE(S):

_____

_____

_____

_____

_____

_____

_____

TITLE: _____

GENRE: _____

SERIES: _____

AUTHOR: _____

PAGES: _____

STARTED: _____

FINISHED: _____

☆☆☆☆☆

FORMAT READ: EBOOK / PRINT / AUDIOBOOK

✓ SYNOPSIS/THINGS I LIKED:
_____
_____
_____
_____
_____

🚫 THINGS I DIDN'T LIKE:
_____
_____
_____
_____
_____

✍ FAVORITE QUOTE(S):
_____
_____
_____
_____
_____
_____
_____

✓ **SYNOPSIS/THINGS I LIKED:**

_____
_____
_____
_____
_____

🚫 **THINGS I DIDN'T LIKE:**

_____
_____
_____
_____
_____

✏️ **FAVORITE QUOTE(S):**

_____
_____
_____
_____
_____
_____
_____

TITLE: _____

GENRE: _____

SERIES: _____

AUTHOR: _____

PAGES: _____

STARTED: _____

FINISHED: _____

☆ ☆ ☆ ☆ ☆

FORMAT READ: EBOOK / PRINT / AUDIOBOOK

151

☑ **SYNOPSIS/THINGS I LIKED:**

_____

_____

_____

_____

_____

🚫 **THINGS I DIDN'T LIKE:**

_____

_____

_____

_____

_____

📝 **FAVORITE QUOTE(S):**

_____

_____

_____

_____

_____

_____

_____

TITLE: _____

GENRE: _____

SERIES: _____

AUTHOR: _____

PAGES: _____

STARTED: _____

FINISHED: _____

☆ ☆ ☆ ☆ ☆

FORMAT READ: EBOOK / PRINT / AUDIOBOOK

TITLE: _____

GENRE: _____

SERIES: _____

AUTHOR: _____

PAGES: _____

STARTED: _____

FINISHED: _____

☆☆☆☆☆

FORMAT READ: EBOOK / PRINT / AUDIOBOOK

☑ **SYNOPSIS/THINGS I LIKED:**

_____
_____
_____
_____

🚫 **THINGS I DIDN'T LIKE:**

_____
_____
_____
_____

✎ **FAVORITE QUOTE(S):**

_____
_____
_____
_____
_____
_____

TITLE: _____

GENRE: _____

SERIES: _____

AUTHOR: _____

PAGES: _____

STARTED: _____

FINISHED: _____

☆☆☆☆☆

FORMAT READ: EBOOK / PRINT / AUDIOBOOK

✓ SYNOPSIS/THINGS I LIKED:

_____
_____
_____
_____
_____

🚫 THINGS I DIDN'T LIKE:

_____
_____
_____
_____
_____

📝 FAVORITE QUOTE(S):

_____
_____
_____
_____
_____
_____
_____
_____

✔ **SYNOPSIS/THINGS I LIKED:**

_____

_____

_____

_____

🚫 **THINGS I DIDN'T LIKE:**

_____

_____

_____

_____

📝 **FAVORITE QUOTE(S):**

_____

_____

_____

_____

_____

_____

TITLE: _____

GENRE: _____

SERIES: _____

AUTHOR: _____

PAGES: _____

STARTED: _____

FINISHED: _____

☆ ☆ ☆ ☆ ☆

FORMAT READ: EBOOK / PRINT / AUDIOBOOK

✔ **SYNOPSIS/THINGS I LIKED:**

_____
_____
_____
_____
_____

🚫 **THINGS I DIDN'T LIKE:**

_____
_____
_____
_____

✏️ **FAVORITE QUOTE(S):**

_____
_____
_____
_____
_____
_____

TITLE: _____

GENRE: _____

SERIES: _____

AUTHOR: _____

PAGES: _____

STARTED: _____

FINISHED: _____

☆ ☆ ☆ ☆ ☆

FORMAT READ: EBOOK / PRINT / AUDIOBOOK

TITLE: _____

GENRE: _____

SERIES: _____

AUTHOR: _____

PAGES: _____

STARTED: _____

FINISHED: _____

☆☆☆☆☆

FORMAT READ: EBOOK / PRINT / AUDIOBOOK

✓ SYNOPSIS/THINGS I LIKED:

_____
_____
_____
_____

🚫 THINGS I DIDN'T LIKE:

_____
_____
_____
_____

✎ FAVORITE QUOTE(S):

_____
_____
_____
_____
_____
_____
_____
_____

TITLE: _____

GENRE: _____

SERIES: _____

AUTHOR: _____

PAGES: _____

STARTED: _____

FINISHED: _____

☆ ☆ ☆ ☆ ☆

FORMAT READ: EBOOK / PRINT / AUDIOBOOK

✓ **SYNOPSIS/THINGS I LIKED:**

_____
_____
_____
_____

🚫 **THINGS I DIDN'T LIKE:**

_____
_____
_____
_____

✎ **FAVORITE QUOTE(S):**

_____
_____
_____
_____
_____
_____

☑ **Synopsis/Things I liked:**

_____
_____
_____
_____

🚫 **Things I didn't like:**

_____
_____
_____
_____

📝 **Favorite quote(s):**

_____
_____
_____
_____
_____
_____

Title: _____

Genre: _____

Series: _____

Author: _____

Pages: _____

Started: _____

Finished: _____

☆ ☆ ☆ ☆ ☆

Format read: Ebook / Print / Audiobook

✓ **SYNOPSIS/THINGS I LIKED:**

_____

_____

_____

_____

🚫 **THINGS I DIDN'T LIKE:**

_____

_____

_____

_____

✏️ **FAVORITE QUOTE(S):**

_____

_____

_____

_____

_____

_____

TITLE: _____

GENRE: _____

SERIES: _____

AUTHOR: _____

PAGES: _____

STARTED: _____

FINISHED: _____

☆ ☆ ☆ ☆ ☆

FORMAT READ: EBOOK / PRINT / AUDIOBOOK

TITLE: _____

GENRE: _____

SERIES: _____

AUTHOR: _____

PAGES: _____

STARTED: _____

FINISHED: _____

☆ ☆ ☆ ☆ ☆

FORMAT READ: EBOOK / PRINT / AUDIOBOOK

☑ SYNOPSIS/THINGS I LIKED:

_____
_____
_____
_____

🚫 THINGS I DIDN'T LIKE:

_____
_____
_____
_____

✎ FAVORITE QUOTE(S):

_____
_____
_____
_____
_____
_____
_____

TITLE: _____

GENRE: _____

SERIES: _____

AUTHOR: _____

PAGES: _____

STARTED: _____

FINISHED: _____

☆☆☆☆☆

FORMAT READ: EBOOK / PRINT / AUDIOBOOK

☑ **SYNOPSIS/THINGS I LIKED:**

_____
_____
_____
_____

🚫 **THINGS I DIDN'T LIKE:**

_____
_____
_____
_____

✎ **FAVORITE QUOTE(S):**

_____
_____
_____
_____
_____
_____
_____

☑ **Synopsis/Things I liked:**

_____

_____

_____

_____

🚫 **Things I didn't like:**

_____

_____

_____

_____

📝 **Favorite quote(s):**

_____

_____

_____

_____

_____

_____

_____

Title: _____

Genre: _____

Series: _____

Author: _____

Pages: _____

Started: _____

Finished: _____

☆ ☆ ☆ ☆ ☆

Format read: Ebook / Print / Audiobook

✓ SYNOPSIS/THINGS I LIKED:

_____
_____
_____
_____
_____

🚫 THINGS I DIDN'T LIKE:

_____
_____
_____
_____
_____

✎ FAVORITE QUOTE(S):

_____
_____
_____
_____
_____
_____
_____
_____

TITLE: _____

GENRE: _____

SERIES: _____

AUTHOR: _____

PAGES: _____

STARTED: _____

FINISHED: _____

☆ ☆ ☆ ☆ ☆

FORMAT READ: EBOOK / PRINT / AUDIOBOOK

TITLE: _____

GENRE: _____

SERIES: _____

AUTHOR: _____

PAGES: _____

STARTED: _____

FINISHED: _____

☆ ☆ ☆ ☆ ☆

FORMAT READ: EBOOK / PRINT / AUDIOBOOK

✔ SYNOPSIS/THINGS I LIKED:

_____
_____
_____
_____

🚫 THINGS I DIDN'T LIKE:

_____
_____
_____
_____

✏ FAVORITE QUOTE(S):

_____
_____
_____
_____
_____
_____
_____

TITLE: _____

GENRE: _____

SERIES: _____

AUTHOR: _____

PAGES: _____

STARTED: _____

FINISHED: _____

☆☆☆☆☆

FORMAT READ: EBOOK / PRINT / AUDIOBOOK

☑ **SYNOPSIS/THINGS I LIKED:**

_____
_____
_____
_____

🚫 **THINGS I DIDN'T LIKE:**

_____
_____
_____
_____

📝 **FAVORITE QUOTE(S):**

_____
_____
_____
_____
_____
_____

✔ Synopsis/Things I liked:

_____
_____
_____
_____
_____

🚫 Things I didn't like:

_____
_____
_____
_____
_____

✎ Favorite quote(s):

_____
_____
_____
_____
_____
_____
_____

Title: _____

Genre: _____

Series: _____

Author: _____

Pages: _____

Started: _____

Finished: _____

☆ ☆ ☆ ☆ ☆

Format read: Ebook / Print / Audiobook

167

☑ **SYNOPSIS/THINGS I LIKED:**

_____
_____
_____
_____

🚫 **THINGS I DIDN'T LIKE:**

_____
_____
_____
_____

📝 **FAVORITE QUOTE(S):**

_____
_____
_____
_____
_____
_____

TITLE: _____

GENRE: _____

SERIES: _____

AUTHOR: _____

PAGES: _____

STARTED: _____

FINISHED: _____

☆ ☆ ☆ ☆ ☆

FORMAT READ: EBOOK / PRINT / AUDIOBOOK

TITLE: _____

GENRE: _____

SERIES: _____

AUTHOR: _____

PAGES: _____

STARTED: _____

FINISHED: _____

☆ ☆ ☆ ☆ ☆

FORMAT READ: EBOOK / PRINT / AUDIOBOOK

✓ **SYNOPSIS/THINGS I LIKED:**

_____
_____
_____
_____
_____

🚫 **THINGS I DIDN'T LIKE:**

_____
_____
_____
_____

✏️ **FAVORITE QUOTE(S):**

_____
_____
_____
_____
_____
_____
_____

TITLE: _____

GENRE: _____

SERIES: _____

AUTHOR: _____

PAGES: _____

STARTED: _____

FINISHED: _____

☆☆☆☆☆

FORMAT READ: EBOOK / PRINT / AUDIOBOOK

✓ **SYNOPSIS/THINGS I LIKED:**

_____
_____
_____
_____
_____

🚫 **THINGS I DIDN'T LIKE:**

_____
_____
_____
_____
_____

✎ **FAVORITE QUOTE(S):**

_____
_____
_____
_____
_____
_____
_____
_____

✓ **SYNOPSIS/THINGS I LIKED:**

_____

_____

_____

_____

⊘ **THINGS I DIDN'T LIKE:**

_____

_____

_____

_____

✎ **FAVORITE QUOTE(S):**

_____

_____

_____

_____

_____

_____

TITLE: _____

GENRE: _____

SERIES: _____

AUTHOR: _____

PAGES: _____

STARTED: _____

FINISHED: _____

☆ ☆ ☆ ☆ ☆

FORMAT READ: EBOOK / PRINT / AUDIOBOOK

✔️ **Synopsis/Things I liked:**

_____
_____
_____
_____

🚫 **Things I didn't like:**

_____
_____
_____
_____

✏️ **Favorite quote(s):**

_____
_____
_____
_____
_____
_____

Title: _____

Genre: _____

Series: _____

Author: _____

Pages: _____

Started: _____

Finished: _____

☆ ☆ ☆ ☆ ☆

Format read: Ebook / Print / Audiobook

TITLE: _____

GENRE: _____

SERIES: _____

AUTHOR: _____

PAGES: _____

STARTED: _____

FINISHED: _____

☆☆☆☆☆

FORMAT READ: EBOOK / PRINT / AUDIOBOOK

✓ SYNOPSIS/THINGS I LIKED:
_____
_____
_____
_____
_____

🚫 THINGS I DIDN'T LIKE:
_____
_____
_____
_____

✎ FAVORITE QUOTE(S):
_____
_____
_____
_____
_____
_____
_____

TITLE: _____

GENRE: _____

SERIES: _____

AUTHOR: _____

PAGES: _____

STARTED: _____

FINISHED: _____

☆☆☆☆☆

FORMAT READ: EBOOK / PRINT / AUDIOBOOK

✓ **SYNOPSIS/THINGS I LIKED:**

_____
_____
_____
_____

🚫 **THINGS I DIDN'T LIKE:**

_____
_____
_____
_____

✎ **FAVORITE QUOTE(S):**

_____
_____
_____
_____
_____
_____

✓ SYNOPSIS/THINGS I LIKED:

_____
_____
_____
_____

⊘ THINGS I DIDN'T LIKE:

_____
_____
_____
_____

✎ FAVORITE QUOTE(S):

_____
_____
_____
_____
_____
_____

TITLE: _____

GENRE: _____

SERIES: _____

AUTHOR: _____

PAGES: _____

STARTED: _____

FINISHED: _____

☆ ☆ ☆ ☆ ☆

FORMAT READ: EBOOK / PRINT / AUDIOBOOK

175

☑ **SYNOPSIS/THINGS I LIKED:**

_____
_____
_____
_____

🚫 **THINGS I DIDN'T LIKE:**

_____
_____
_____
_____

📝 **FAVORITE QUOTE(S):**

_____
_____
_____
_____
_____
_____

TITLE: _____

GENRE: _____

SERIES: _____

AUTHOR: _____

PAGES: _____

STARTED: _____

FINISHED: _____

☆ ☆ ☆ ☆ ☆

FORMAT READ: EBOOK / PRINT / AUDIOBOOK

TITLE: _____

GENRE: _____

SERIES: _____

AUTHOR: _____

PAGES: _____

STARTED: _____

FINISHED: _____

☆ ☆ ☆ ☆ ☆

FORMAT READ: EBOOK / PRINT / AUDIOBOOK

✓ **SYNOPSIS/THINGS I LIKED:**

_____
_____
_____
_____

🚫 **THINGS I DIDN'T LIKE:**

_____
_____
_____
_____

✎ **FAVORITE QUOTE(S):**

_____
_____
_____
_____
_____
_____

TITLE: _____

GENRE: _____

SERIES: _____

AUTHOR: _____

PAGES: _____

STARTED: _____

FINISHED: _____

☆ ☆ ☆ ☆ ☆

FORMAT READ: EBOOK / PRINT / AUDIOBOOK

✅ **SYNOPSIS/THINGS I LIKED:**

_____
_____
_____
_____

🚫 **THINGS I DIDN'T LIKE:**

_____
_____
_____
_____

📝 **FAVORITE QUOTE(S):**

_____
_____
_____
_____
_____
_____
_____

☑ SYNOPSIS/THINGS I LIKED:

_____
_____
_____
_____

🚫 THINGS I DIDN'T LIKE:

_____
_____
_____
_____

✎ FAVORITE QUOTE(S):

_____
_____
_____
_____
_____
_____

TITLE: _____

GENRE: _____

SERIES: _____

AUTHOR: _____

PAGES: _____

STARTED: _____

FINISHED: _____

☆ ☆ ☆ ☆ ☆

FORMAT READ: EBOOK / PRINT / AUDIOBOOK

✓ **Synopsis/Things I liked:**

_____

_____

_____

_____

🚫 **Things I didn't like:**

_____

_____

_____

_____

✎ **Favorite quote(s):**

_____

_____

_____

_____

_____

_____

Title: _____

Genre: _____

Series: _____

Author: _____

Pages: _____

Started: _____

Finished: _____

☆ ☆ ☆ ☆ ☆

Format read: Ebook / Print / Audiobook

TITLE: _____

GENRE: _____

SERIES: _____

AUTHOR: _____

PAGES: _____

STARTED: _____

FINISHED: _____

☆☆☆☆☆

FORMAT READ: EBOOK / PRINT / AUDIOBOOK

✓ SYNOPSIS/THINGS I LIKED:

_____

_____

_____

_____

🚫 THINGS I DIDN'T LIKE:

_____

_____

_____

_____

✎ FAVORITE QUOTE(S):

_____

_____

_____

_____

_____

_____

_____

TITLE: _____

GENRE: _____

SERIES: _____

AUTHOR: _____

PAGES: _____

STARTED: _____

FINISHED: _____

☆ ☆ ☆ ☆ ☆

FORMAT READ: EBOOK / PRINT / AUDIOBOOK

✓ **SYNOPSIS/THINGS I LIKED:**

_____
_____
_____
_____

🚫 **THINGS I DIDN'T LIKE:**

_____
_____
_____
_____

✎ **FAVORITE QUOTE(S):**

_____
_____
_____
_____
_____
_____
_____

✔ **SYNOPSIS/THINGS I LIKED:**

_____
_____
_____
_____

🚫 **THINGS I DIDN'T LIKE:**

_____
_____
_____
_____

📝 **FAVORITE QUOTE(S):**

_____
_____
_____
_____
_____
_____

TITLE: _____

GENRE: _____

SERIES: _____

AUTHOR: _____

PAGES: _____

STARTED: _____

FINISHED: _____

☆ ☆ ☆ ☆ ☆

FORMAT READ: EBOOK / PRINT / AUDIOBOOK

✓ **SYNOPSIS/THINGS I LIKED:**

_____
_____
_____
_____
_____

🚫 **THINGS I DIDN'T LIKE:**

_____
_____
_____
_____

✎ **FAVORITE QUOTE(S):**

_____
_____
_____
_____
_____
_____

TITLE: _____

GENRE: _____

SERIES: _____

AUTHOR: _____

PAGES: _____

STARTED: _____

FINISHED: _____

☆ ☆ ☆ ☆ ☆

FORMAT READ: EBOOK / PRINT / AUDIOBOOK

TITLE: _____

GENRE: _____

SERIES: _____

AUTHOR: _____

PAGES: _____

STARTED: _____

FINISHED: _____

☆ ☆ ☆ ☆ ☆

FORMAT READ: EBOOK / PRINT / AUDIOBOOK

✓ SYNOPSIS/THINGS I LIKED:

_____
_____
_____
_____

🚫 THINGS I DIDN'T LIKE:

_____
_____
_____
_____

✎ FAVORITE QUOTE(S):

_____
_____
_____
_____
_____
_____
_____

TITLE: _____

GENRE: _____

SERIES: _____

AUTHOR: _____

PAGES: _____

STARTED: _____

FINISHED: _____

☆☆☆☆☆

FORMAT READ: EBOOK / PRINT / AUDIOBOOK

✓ **SYNOPSIS/THINGS I LIKED:**

_____
_____
_____
_____

🚫 **THINGS I DIDN'T LIKE:**

_____
_____
_____
_____

✍ **FAVORITE QUOTE(S):**

_____
_____
_____
_____
_____
_____

✓ **SYNOPSIS/THINGS I LIKED:**

_____
_____
_____
_____

🚫 **THINGS I DIDN'T LIKE:**

_____
_____
_____
_____

✎ **FAVORITE QUOTE(S):**

_____
_____
_____
_____
_____
_____

TITLE: _____

GENRE: _____

SERIES: _____

AUTHOR: _____

PAGES: _____

STARTED: _____

FINISHED: _____

☆ ☆ ☆ ☆ ☆

FORMAT READ: EBOOK / PRINT / AUDIOBOOK

_____
_____
_____
_____
_____

🚫 THINGS I DIDN'T LIKE:

_____
_____
_____
_____
_____

✎ FAVORITE QUOTE(S):

_____
_____
_____
_____
_____
_____
_____

TITLE: _____

GENRE: _____

SERIES: _____

AUTHOR: _____

PAGES: _____

STARTED: _____

FINISHED: _____

☆ ☆ ☆ ☆ ☆

FORMAT READ: EBOOK / PRINT / AUDIOBOOK

TITLE: _____

GENRE: _____

SERIES: _____

AUTHOR: _____

PAGES: _____

STARTED: _____

FINISHED: _____

☆☆☆☆☆

FORMAT READ: EBOOK / PRINT / AUDIOBOOK

✓ SYNOPSIS/THINGS I LIKED:

_____
_____
_____
_____

⊘ THINGS I DIDN'T LIKE:

_____
_____
_____
_____

✎ FAVORITE QUOTE(S):

_____
_____
_____
_____
_____
_____

TITLE: _____

GENRE: _____

SERIES: _____

AUTHOR: _____

PAGES: _____

STARTED: _____

FINISHED: _____

☆☆☆☆☆

FORMAT READ: EBOOK / PRINT / AUDIOBOOK

☑ **SYNOPSIS/THINGS I LIKED:**

_____
_____
_____
_____
_____

⃠ **THINGS I DIDN'T LIKE:**

_____
_____
_____
_____
_____

✎ **FAVORITE QUOTE(S):**

_____
_____
_____
_____
_____
_____
_____

✓ **SYNOPSIS/THINGS I LIKED:**

_____
_____
_____
_____

🚫 **THINGS I DIDN'T LIKE:**

_____
_____
_____
_____

📝 **FAVORITE QUOTE(S):**

_____
_____
_____
_____
_____
_____

TITLE: _____

GENRE: _____

SERIES: _____

AUTHOR: _____

PAGES: _____

STARTED: _____

FINISHED: _____

☆ ☆ ☆ ☆ ☆

FORMAT READ: EBOOK / PRINT / AUDIOBOOK

☑ **SYNOPSIS/THINGS I LIKED:**

_____
_____
_____
_____
_____

🚫 **THINGS I DIDN'T LIKE:**

_____
_____
_____
_____
_____

📝 **FAVORITE QUOTE(S):**

_____
_____
_____
_____
_____
_____
_____

TITLE: _____

GENRE: _____

SERIES: _____

AUTHOR: _____

PAGES: _____

STARTED: _____

FINISHED: _____

☆ ☆ ☆ ☆ ☆

FORMAT READ: EBOOK / PRINT / AUDIOBOOK

TITLE: _____

GENRE: _____

SERIES: _____

AUTHOR: _____

PAGES: _____

STARTED: _____

FINISHED: _____

☆ ☆ ☆ ☆ ☆

FORMAT READ: EBOOK / PRINT / AUDIOBOOK

✅ SYNOPSIS/THINGS I LIKED:

_____
_____
_____
_____
_____

🚫 THINGS I DIDN'T LIKE:

_____
_____
_____
_____

📝 FAVORITE QUOTE(S):

_____
_____
_____
_____
_____
_____
_____

TITLE: _____

GENRE: _____

SERIES: _____

AUTHOR: _____

PAGES: _____

STARTED: _____

FINISHED: _____

☆☆☆☆☆

FORMAT READ: EBOOK / PRINT / AUDIOBOOK

☑ **SYNOPSIS/THINGS I LIKED:**

_____
_____
_____
_____

🚫 **THINGS I DIDN'T LIKE:**

_____
_____
_____
_____

✎ **FAVORITE QUOTE(S):**

_____
_____
_____
_____
_____
_____
_____

☑ **SYNOPSIS/THINGS I LIKED:**

_____
_____
_____
_____
_____

🚫 **THINGS I DIDN'T LIKE:**

_____
_____
_____
_____

✎ **FAVORITE QUOTE(S):**

_____
_____
_____
_____
_____
_____

TITLE: _____

GENRE: _____

SERIES: _____

AUTHOR: _____

PAGES: _____

STARTED: _____

FINISHED: _____

☆ ☆ ☆ ☆ ☆

FORMAT READ: EBOOK / PRINT / AUDIOBOOK

☑ **SYNOPSIS/THINGS I LIKED:**

_____
_____
_____
_____

🚫 **THINGS I DIDN'T LIKE:**

_____
_____
_____
_____

✎ **FAVORITE QUOTE(S):**

_____
_____
_____
_____
_____
_____

TITLE: _____

GENRE: _____

SERIES: _____

AUTHOR: _____

PAGES: _____

STARTED: _____

FINISHED: _____

☆ ☆ ☆ ☆ ☆

FORMAT READ: EBOOK / PRINT / AUDIOBOOK

TITLE: _____

GENRE: _____

SERIES: _____

AUTHOR: _____

PAGES: _____

STARTED: _____

FINISHED: _____

☆☆☆☆☆

FORMAT READ: EBOOK / PRINT / AUDIOBOOK

SYNOPSIS/THINGS I LIKED:

_____
_____
_____
_____
_____

THINGS I DIDN'T LIKE:

_____
_____
_____
_____
_____

FAVORITE QUOTE(S):

_____
_____
_____
_____
_____
_____
_____

TITLE: _____

GENRE: _____

SERIES: _____

AUTHOR: _____

PAGES: _____

STARTED: _____

FINISHED: _____

☆ ☆ ☆ ☆ ☆

FORMAT READ: EBOOK / PRINT / AUDIOBOOK

☑ **SYNOPSIS/THINGS I LIKED:**

_____
_____
_____
_____

🚫 **THINGS I DIDN'T LIKE:**

_____
_____
_____
_____

✎ **FAVORITE QUOTE(S):**

_____
_____
_____
_____
_____
_____

✅ SYNOPSIS/THINGS I LIKED:

_____
_____
_____
_____
_____

🚫 THINGS I DIDN'T LIKE:

_____
_____
_____
_____
_____

✏️ FAVORITE QUOTE(S):

_____
_____
_____
_____
_____
_____
_____

TITLE: _____

GENRE: _____

SERIES: _____

AUTHOR: _____

PAGES: _____

STARTED: _____

FINISHED: _____

☆ ☆ ☆ ☆ ☆

FORMAT READ: EBOOK / PRINT / AUDIOBOOK

✓ SYNOPSIS/THINGS I LIKED:

_____
_____
_____
_____

🚫 THINGS I DIDN'T LIKE:

_____
_____
_____
_____

✎ FAVORITE QUOTE(S):

_____
_____
_____
_____
_____
_____

TITLE: _____

GENRE: _____

SERIES: _____

AUTHOR: _____

PAGES: _____

STARTED: _____

FINISHED: _____

☆ ☆ ☆ ☆ ☆

FORMAT READ: EBOOK / PRINT / AUDIOBOOK

TITLE: _____

GENRE: _____

SERIES: _____

AUTHOR: _____

PAGES: _____

STARTED: _____

FINISHED: _____

☆☆☆☆☆

FORMAT READ: EBOOK / PRINT / AUDIOBOOK

☑ SYNOPSIS/THINGS I LIKED:

_____
_____
_____
_____
_____

🚫 THINGS I DIDN'T LIKE:

_____
_____
_____
_____
_____

✒ FAVORITE QUOTE(S):

_____
_____
_____
_____
_____
_____
_____

TITLE: _____

GENRE: _____

SERIES: _____

AUTHOR: _____

PAGES: _____

STARTED: _____

FINISHED: _____

☆ ☆ ☆ ☆ ☆

FORMAT READ: EBOOK / PRINT / AUDIOBOOK

✓ **SYNOPSIS/THINGS I LIKED:**

_____
_____
_____
_____

🚫 **THINGS I DIDN'T LIKE:**

_____
_____
_____
_____

✎ **FAVORITE QUOTE(S):**

_____
_____
_____
_____
_____
_____
_____

✓ **SYNOPSIS/THINGS I LIKED:**

_____
_____
_____
_____

⊘ **THINGS I DIDN'T LIKE:**

_____
_____
_____
_____

✎ **FAVORITE QUOTE(S):**

_____
_____
_____
_____
_____
_____

TITLE: _____

GENRE: _____

SERIES: _____

AUTHOR: _____

PAGES: _____

STARTED: _____

FINISHED: _____

☆ ☆ ☆ ☆ ☆

FORMAT READ: EBOOK / PRINT / AUDIOBOOK

_____

_____

_____

_____

🚫 THINGS I DIDN'T LIKE:

_____

_____

_____

_____

📝 FAVORITE QUOTE(S):

_____

_____

_____

_____

_____

_____

TITLE: _____

GENRE: _____

SERIES: _____

AUTHOR: _____

PAGES: _____

STARTED: _____

FINISHED: _____

☆ ☆ ☆ ☆ ☆

FORMAT READ: EBOOK / PRINT / AUDIOBOOK

TITLE: _____

GENRE: _____

SERIES: _____

AUTHOR: _____

PAGES: _____

STARTED: _____

FINISHED: _____

☆ ☆ ☆ ☆ ☆

FORMAT READ: EBOOK / PRINT / AUDIOBOOK

✔ **SYNOPSIS/THINGS I LIKED:**

_____

_____

_____

_____

🚫 **THINGS I DIDN'T LIKE:**

_____

_____

_____

_____

✏️ **FAVORITE QUOTE(S):**

_____

_____

_____

_____

_____

_____

_____

TITLE: _____

GENRE: _____

SERIES: _____

AUTHOR: _____

PAGES: _____

STARTED: _____

FINISHED: _____

☆☆☆☆☆

FORMAT READ: EBOOK / PRINT / AUDIOBOOK

☑ SYNOPSIS/THINGS I LIKED:
_____
_____
_____
_____

🚫 THINGS I DIDN'T LIKE:
_____
_____
_____
_____

✏ FAVORITE QUOTE(S):
_____
_____
_____
_____
_____
_____

☑ **Synopsis/Things I liked:**

_____

_____

_____

_____

_____

🚫 **Things I didn't like:**

_____

_____

_____

_____

📝 **Favorite quote(s):**

_____

_____

_____

_____

_____

_____

Title: _____

Genre: _____

Series: _____

Author: _____

Pages: _____

Started: _____

Finished: _____

☆ ☆ ☆ ☆ ☆

Format read: Ebook / Print / Audiobook

✔ **SYNOPSIS/THINGS I LIKED:**

_____

_____

_____

_____

_____

🚫 **THINGS I DIDN'T LIKE:**

_____

_____

_____

_____

✏️ **FAVORITE QUOTE(S):**

_____

_____

_____

_____

_____

_____

TITLE: _____

GENRE: _____

SERIES: _____

AUTHOR: _____

PAGES: _____

STARTED: _____

FINISHED: _____

☆ ☆ ☆ ☆ ☆

FORMAT READ: EBOOK / PRINT / AUDIOBOOK

TITLE: _____

GENRE: _____

SERIES: _____

AUTHOR: _____

PAGES: _____

STARTED: _____

FINISHED: _____

☆ ☆ ☆ ☆ ☆

FORMAT READ: EBOOK / PRINT / AUDIOBOOK

☑ **SYNOPSIS/THINGS I LIKED:**

_____
_____
_____
_____

🚫 **THINGS I DIDN'T LIKE:**

_____
_____
_____
_____

✎ **FAVORITE QUOTE(S):**

_____
_____
_____
_____
_____
_____
_____

TITLE: _____

GENRE: _____

SERIES: _____

AUTHOR: _____

PAGES: _____

STARTED: _____

FINISHED: _____

☆☆☆☆☆

FORMAT READ: EBOOK / PRINT / AUDIOBOOK

✓ **SYNOPSIS/THINGS I LIKED:**

_____
_____
_____
_____

🚫 **THINGS I DIDN'T LIKE:**

_____
_____
_____
_____

✎ **FAVORITE QUOTE(S):**

_____
_____
_____
_____
_____
_____

☑ **Synopsis/Things I liked:**

_____

_____

_____

_____

_____

🚫 **Things I didn't like:**

_____

_____

_____

_____

_____

✏️ **Favorite quote(s):**

_____

_____

_____

_____

_____

_____

_____

Title: _____

Genre: _____

Series: _____

Author: _____

Pages: _____

Started: _____

Finished: _____

☆ ☆ ☆ ☆ ☆

Format read: Ebook / Print / Audiobook

✅ **SYNOPSIS/THINGS I LIKED:**

_____
_____
_____
_____
_____

🚫 **THINGS I DIDN'T LIKE:**

_____
_____
_____
_____
_____

📝 **FAVORITE QUOTE(S):**

_____
_____
_____
_____
_____
_____
_____

TITLE: _____

GENRE: _____

SERIES: _____

AUTHOR: _____

PAGES: _____

STARTED: _____

FINISHED: _____

☆ ☆ ☆ ☆ ☆

FORMAT READ: EBOOK / PRINT / AUDIOBOOK

TITLE: _____

GENRE: _____

SERIES: _____

AUTHOR: _____

PAGES: _____

STARTED: _____

FINISHED: _____

☆ ☆ ☆ ☆ ☆

FORMAT READ: EBOOK / PRINT / AUDIOBOOK

☑ **SYNOPSIS/THINGS I LIKED:**

_____
_____
_____
_____

🚫 **THINGS I DIDN'T LIKE:**

_____
_____
_____
_____

✎ **FAVORITE QUOTE(S):**

_____
_____
_____
_____
_____
_____

TITLE: _____

GENRE: _____

SERIES: _____

AUTHOR: _____

PAGES: _____

STARTED: _____

FINISHED: _____

☆ ☆ ☆ ☆ ☆

FORMAT READ: EBOOK / PRINT / AUDIOBOOK

✔ **SYNOPSIS/THINGS I LIKED:**

_____
_____
_____
_____
_____

🚫 **THINGS I DIDN'T LIKE:**

_____
_____
_____
_____

✎ **FAVORITE QUOTE(S):**

_____
_____
_____
_____
_____
_____
_____

☑ Synopsis/Things I liked:

_____
_____
_____
_____
_____

🚫 Things I didn't like:

_____
_____
_____
_____

✎ Favorite quote(s):

_____
_____
_____
_____
_____
_____

Title: _____

Genre: _____

Series: _____

Author: _____

Pages: _____

Started: _____

Finished: _____

☆ ☆ ☆ ☆ ☆

Format read: Ebook / Print / Audiobook

215

✅ **Synopsis/Things I liked:**

_____

_____

_____

_____

🚫 **Things I didn't like:**

_____

_____

_____

_____

✏️ **Favorite quote(s):**

_____

_____

_____

_____

_____

_____

Title: _____

Genre: _____

Series: _____

Author: _____

Pages: _____

Started: _____

Finished: _____

⭐ ⭐ ⭐ ⭐ ⭐

Format read: Ebook / Print / Audiobook

TITLE: _____

GENRE: _____

SERIES: _____

AUTHOR: _____

PAGES: _____

STARTED: _____

FINISHED: _____

☆ ☆ ☆ ☆ ☆

FORMAT READ: EBOOK / PRINT / AUDIOBOOK

✅ **SYNOPSIS/THINGS I LIKED:**

_____
_____
_____
_____

🚫 **THINGS I DIDN'T LIKE:**

_____
_____
_____
_____

📝 **FAVORITE QUOTE(S):**

_____
_____
_____
_____
_____
_____
_____

TITLE: _____

GENRE: _____

SERIES: _____

AUTHOR: _____

PAGES: _____

STARTED: _____

FINISHED: _____

☆☆☆☆☆

FORMAT READ: EBOOK / PRINT / AUDIOBOOK

✓ SYNOPSIS/THINGS I LIKED:

_____
_____
_____
_____

🚫 THINGS I DIDN'T LIKE:

_____
_____
_____
_____

✏️ FAVORITE QUOTE(S):

_____
_____
_____
_____
_____
_____
_____

☑ **SYNOPSIS/THINGS I LIKED:**

_____
_____
_____
_____
_____

🚫 **THINGS I DIDN'T LIKE:**

_____
_____
_____
_____

✎ **FAVORITE QUOTE(S):**

_____
_____
_____
_____
_____
_____
_____

TITLE: _____

GENRE: _____

SERIES: _____

AUTHOR: _____

PAGES: _____

STARTED: _____

FINISHED: _____

☆☆☆☆☆

FORMAT READ: EBOOK / PRINT / AUDIOBOOK

✓ **SYNOPSIS/THINGS I LIKED:**

_____

_____

_____

_____

_____

🚫 **THINGS I DIDN'T LIKE:**

_____

_____

_____

_____

📝 **FAVORITE QUOTE(S):**

_____

_____

_____

_____

_____

_____

TITLE: _____

GENRE: _____

SERIES: _____

AUTHOR: _____

PAGES: _____

STARTED: _____

FINISHED: _____

☆ ☆ ☆ ☆ ☆

FORMAT READ: EBOOK / PRINT / AUDIOBOOK

TITLE: _____

GENRE: _____

SERIES: _____

AUTHOR: _____

PAGES: _____

STARTED: _____

FINISHED: _____

☆☆☆☆☆

FORMAT READ: EBOOK / PRINT / AUDIOBOOK

✓ SYNOPSIS/THINGS I LIKED:
_____
_____
_____
_____
_____

🚫 THINGS I DIDN'T LIKE:
_____
_____
_____
_____
_____

✎ FAVORITE QUOTE(S):
_____
_____
_____
_____
_____
_____
_____
_____

TITLE: _____

GENRE: _____

SERIES: _____

AUTHOR: _____

PAGES: _____

STARTED: _____

FINISHED: _____

☆☆☆☆☆

FORMAT READ: EBOOK / PRINT / AUDIOBOOK

✓ **SYNOPSIS/THINGS I LIKED:** _____

_____

_____

_____

_____

🚫 **THINGS I DIDN'T LIKE:** _____

_____

_____

_____

_____

📝 **FAVORITE QUOTE(S):** _____

_____

_____

_____

_____

_____

_____

_____

✓ SYNOPSIS/THINGS I LIKED:

_____
_____
_____
_____
_____

🚫 THINGS I DIDN'T LIKE:

_____
_____
_____
_____
_____

✎ FAVORITE QUOTE(S):

_____
_____
_____
_____
_____
_____
_____

TITLE: _____

GENRE: _____

SERIES: _____

AUTHOR: _____

PAGES: _____

STARTED: _____

FINISHED: _____

☆ ☆ ☆ ☆ ☆

FORMAT READ: EBOOK / PRINT / AUDIOBOOK

223

✓ **SYNOPSIS/THINGS I LIKED:**

_____

_____

_____

_____

🚫 **THINGS I DIDN'T LIKE:**

_____

_____

_____

_____

✎ **FAVORITE QUOTE(S):**

_____

_____

_____

_____

_____

_____

TITLE: _____

GENRE: _____

SERIES: _____

AUTHOR: _____

PAGES: _____

STARTED: _____

FINISHED: _____

☆ ☆ ☆ ☆ ☆

FORMAT READ: EBOOK / PRINT / AUDIOBOOK

TITLE:

GENRE:

SERIES:

AUTHOR:

PAGES:

STARTED:

FINISHED:

☆☆☆☆☆

FORMAT READ: EBOOK / PRINT / AUDIOBOOK

✓ SYNOPSIS/THINGS I LIKED:

⊘ THINGS I DIDN'T LIKE:

✎ FAVORITE QUOTE(S):

TITLE: _____

GENRE: _____

SERIES: _____

AUTHOR: _____

PAGES: _____

STARTED: _____

FINISHED: _____

☆☆☆☆☆

FORMAT READ: EBOOK / PRINT / AUDIOBOOK

✅ **SYNOPSIS/THINGS I LIKED:**

_____
_____
_____
_____
_____

🚫 **THINGS I DIDN'T LIKE:**

_____
_____
_____
_____
_____

📝 **FAVORITE QUOTE(S):**

_____
_____
_____
_____
_____
_____
_____
_____

☑ SYNOPSIS/THINGS I LIKED:

_____

_____

_____

_____

_____

🚫 THINGS I DIDN'T LIKE:

_____

_____

_____

_____

📝 FAVORITE QUOTE(S):

_____

_____

_____

_____

_____

_____

TITLE: _____

GENRE: _____

SERIES: _____

AUTHOR: _____

PAGES: _____

STARTED: _____

FINISHED: _____

☆ ☆ ☆ ☆ ☆

FORMAT READ: EBOOK / PRINT / AUDIOBOOK

227

✓ **SYNOPSIS/THINGS I LIKED:**

_____
_____
_____
_____
_____

🚫 **THINGS I DIDN'T LIKE:**

_____
_____
_____
_____

📝 **FAVORITE QUOTE(S):**

_____
_____
_____
_____
_____
_____
_____

TITLE: _____

GENRE: _____

SERIES: _____

AUTHOR: _____

PAGES: _____

STARTED: _____

FINISHED: _____

☆ ☆ ☆ ☆ ☆

FORMAT READ: EBOOK / PRINT / AUDIOBOOK

228

TITLE: _____

GENRE: _____

SERIES: _____

AUTHOR: _____

PAGES: _____

STARTED: _____

FINISHED: _____

☆ ☆ ☆ ☆ ☆

FORMAT READ: EBOOK / PRINT / AUDIOBOOK

✅ SYNOPSIS/THINGS I LIKED:

_____
_____
_____
_____
_____

🚫 THINGS I DIDN'T LIKE:

_____
_____
_____
_____
_____

📝 FAVORITE QUOTE(S):

_____
_____
_____
_____
_____
_____
_____

TITLE: _____

GENRE: _____

SERIES: _____

AUTHOR: _____

PAGES: _____

STARTED: _____

FINISHED: _____

☆☆☆☆☆

FORMAT READ: EBOOK / PRINT / AUDIOBOOK

✔️ **SYNOPSIS/THINGS I LIKED:**

_____
_____
_____
_____

🚫 **THINGS I DIDN'T LIKE:**

_____
_____
_____
_____

✏️ **FAVORITE QUOTE(S):**

_____
_____
_____
_____
_____
_____
_____

✔ **Synopsis/Things I liked:**

_____

_____

_____

_____

_____

🚫 **Things I didn't like:**

_____

_____

_____

_____

🖌 **Favorite quote(s):**

_____

_____

_____

_____

_____

_____

Title: _____

Genre: _____

Series: _____

Author: _____

Pages: _____

Started: _____

Finished: _____

☆ ☆ ☆ ☆ ☆

Format read: Ebook / Print / Audiobook

☑️ **SYNOPSIS/THINGS I LIKED:**

_____

_____

_____

_____

_____

🚫 **THINGS I DIDN'T LIKE:**

_____

_____

_____

_____

_____

📝 **FAVORITE QUOTE(S):**

_____

_____

_____

_____

_____

_____

_____

TITLE: _____

GENRE: _____

SERIES: _____

AUTHOR: _____

PAGES: _____

STARTED: _____

FINISHED: _____

☆ ☆ ☆ ☆ ☆

FORMAT READ: EBOOK / PRINT / AUDIOBOOK

TITLE: _____

GENRE: _____

SERIES: _____

AUTHOR: _____

PAGES: _____

STARTED: _____

FINISHED: _____

☆☆☆☆☆

FORMAT READ: EBOOK / PRINT / AUDIOBOOK

SYNOPSIS/THINGS I LIKED:

_____
_____
_____
_____
_____

THINGS I DIDN'T LIKE:

_____
_____
_____
_____
_____

FAVORITE QUOTE(S):

_____
_____
_____
_____
_____
_____
_____
_____

TITLE: _____

GENRE: _____

SERIES: _____

AUTHOR: _____

PAGES: _____

STARTED: _____

FINISHED: _____

☆☆☆☆☆

FORMAT READ: EBOOK / PRINT / AUDIOBOOK

✓ SYNOPSIS/THINGS I LIKED:
_____
_____
_____
_____

🚫 THINGS I DIDN'T LIKE:
_____
_____
_____
_____

✏️ FAVORITE QUOTE(S):
_____
_____
_____
_____
_____
_____

✔ **SYNOPSIS/THINGS I LIKED:**

_____
_____
_____
_____
_____

🚫 **THINGS I DIDN'T LIKE:**

_____
_____
_____
_____
_____

📝 **FAVORITE QUOTE(S):**

_____
_____
_____
_____
_____
_____
_____

TITLE: _____

GENRE: _____

SERIES: _____

AUTHOR: _____

PAGES: _____

STARTED: _____

FINISHED: _____

☆ ☆ ☆ ☆ ☆

FORMAT READ: EBOOK / PRINT / AUDIOBOOK

✓ SYNOPSIS/THINGS I LIKED:

_____
_____
_____
_____

🚫 THINGS I DIDN'T LIKE:

_____
_____
_____
_____

✎ FAVORITE QUOTE(S):

_____
_____
_____
_____
_____
_____

TITLE: _____

GENRE: _____

SERIES: _____

AUTHOR: _____

PAGES: _____

STARTED: _____

FINISHED: _____

☆ ☆ ☆ ☆ ☆

FORMAT READ: EBOOK / PRINT / AUDIOBOOK

TITLE: _____

GENRE: _____

SERIES: _____

AUTHOR: _____

PAGES: _____

STARTED: _____

FINISHED: _____

☆☆☆☆☆

FORMAT READ: EBOOK / PRINT / AUDIOBOOK

☑ **SYNOPSIS/THINGS I LIKED:** _____

_____

_____

_____

🚫 **THINGS I DIDN'T LIKE:** _____

_____

_____

_____

📝 **FAVORITE QUOTE(S):** _____

_____

_____

_____

_____

_____

_____

TITLE: _____

GENRE: _____

SERIES: _____

AUTHOR: _____

PAGES: _____

STARTED: _____

FINISHED: _____

☆ ☆ ☆ ☆ ☆

FORMAT READ: EBOOK / PRINT / AUDIOBOOK

☑ **SYNOPSIS/THINGS I LIKED:**

_____
_____
_____
_____
_____

🚫 **THINGS I DIDN'T LIKE:**

_____
_____
_____
_____

🖊 **FAVORITE QUOTE(S):**

_____
_____
_____
_____
_____
_____
_____

✓ **SYNOPSIS/THINGS I LIKED:**

_____
_____
_____
_____
_____

🚫 **THINGS I DIDN'T LIKE:**

_____
_____
_____
_____
_____

📝 **FAVORITE QUOTE(S):**

_____
_____
_____
_____
_____
_____
_____

TITLE: _____

GENRE: _____

SERIES: _____

AUTHOR: _____

PAGES: _____

STARTED: _____

FINISHED: _____

☆ ☆ ☆ ☆ ☆

FORMAT READ: EBOOK / PRINT / AUDIOBOOK

✔ SYNOPSIS/THINGS I LIKED:

_____
_____
_____
_____

🚫 THINGS I DIDN'T LIKE:

_____
_____
_____
_____

✒ FAVORITE QUOTE(S):

_____
_____
_____
_____
_____
_____

TITLE: _____

GENRE: _____

SERIES: _____

AUTHOR: _____

PAGES: _____

STARTED: _____

FINISHED: _____

☆ ☆ ☆ ☆ ☆

FORMAT READ: EBOOK / PRINT / AUDIOBOOK

240

TITLE: _____

GENRE: _____

SERIES: _____

AUTHOR: _____

PAGES: _____

STARTED: _____

FINISHED: _____

☆ ☆ ☆ ☆ ☆

FORMAT READ: EBOOK / PRINT / AUDIOBOOK

✓ **SYNOPSIS/THINGS I LIKED:**

_____
_____
_____
_____
_____

🚫 **THINGS I DIDN'T LIKE:**

_____
_____
_____
_____

✎ **FAVORITE QUOTE(S):**

_____
_____
_____
_____
_____
_____
_____

TITLE: _____

GENRE: _____

SERIES: _____

AUTHOR: _____

PAGES: _____

STARTED: _____

FINISHED: _____

☆☆☆☆☆

FORMAT READ: EBOOK / PRINT / AUDIOBOOK

☑ **SYNOPSIS/THINGS I LIKED:**

_____
_____
_____
_____

🚫 **THINGS I DIDN'T LIKE:**

_____
_____
_____
_____

✎ **FAVORITE QUOTE(S):**

_____
_____
_____
_____
_____
_____
_____

✓ **SYNOPSIS/THINGS I LIKED:**

_____
_____
_____
_____

🚫 **THINGS I DIDN'T LIKE:**

_____
_____
_____
_____

✎ **FAVORITE QUOTE(S):**

_____
_____
_____
_____
_____
_____

TITLE: _____

GENRE: _____

SERIES: _____

AUTHOR: _____

PAGES: _____

STARTED: _____

FINISHED: _____

☆ ☆ ☆ ☆ ☆

FORMAT READ: EBOOK / PRINT / AUDIOBOOK

✔ **SYNOPSIS/THINGS I LIKED:**

_____
_____
_____
_____

🚫 **THINGS I DIDN'T LIKE:**

_____
_____
_____
_____

📝 **FAVORITE QUOTE(S):**

_____
_____
_____
_____
_____
_____

TITLE: _____

GENRE: _____

SERIES: _____

AUTHOR: _____

PAGES: _____

STARTED: _____

FINISHED: _____

☆ ☆ ☆ ☆ ☆

FORMAT READ: EBOOK / PRINT / AUDIOBOOK

TITLE: _____

GENRE: _____

SERIES: _____

AUTHOR: _____

PAGES: _____

STARTED: _____

FINISHED: _____

☆ ☆ ☆ ☆ ☆

FORMAT READ: EBOOK / PRINT / AUDIOBOOK

✓ **SYNOPSIS/THINGS I LIKED:**

_____
_____
_____
_____

🚫 **THINGS I DIDN'T LIKE:**

_____
_____
_____
_____

✏️ **FAVORITE QUOTE(S):**

_____
_____
_____
_____
_____
_____
_____

TITLE: _____

GENRE: _____

SERIES: _____

AUTHOR: _____

PAGES: _____

STARTED: _____

FINISHED: _____

☆☆☆☆☆

FORMAT READ: EBOOK / PRINT / AUDIOBOOK

✔ SYNOPSIS/THINGS I LIKED:
_____
_____
_____
_____
_____

🚫 THINGS I DIDN'T LIKE:
_____
_____
_____
_____
_____

✎ FAVORITE QUOTE(S):
_____
_____
_____
_____
_____
_____
_____

✔️ **SYNOPSIS/THINGS I LIKED:**

_____
_____
_____
_____
_____

🚫 **THINGS I DIDN'T LIKE:**

_____
_____
_____
_____
_____

✏️ **FAVORITE QUOTE(S):**

_____
_____
_____
_____
_____
_____
_____

TITLE: _____

GENRE: _____

SERIES: _____

AUTHOR: _____

PAGES: _____

STARTED: _____

FINISHED: _____

☆ ☆ ☆ ☆ ☆

FORMAT READ: EBOOK / PRINT / AUDIOBOOK

☑ **SYNOPSIS/THINGS I LIKED:**

_____

_____

_____

_____

🚫 **THINGS I DIDN'T LIKE:**

_____

_____

_____

_____

✎ **FAVORITE QUOTE(S):**

_____

_____

_____

_____

_____

_____

TITLE: _____

GENRE: _____

SERIES: _____

AUTHOR: _____

PAGES: _____

STARTED: _____

FINISHED: _____

☆ ☆ ☆ ☆ ☆

FORMAT READ: EBOOK / PRINT / AUDIOBOOK

Title: _____

Genre: _____

Series: _____

Author: _____

Pages: _____

Started: _____

Finished: _____

☆ ☆ ☆ ☆ ☆

FORMAT READ: EBOOK / PRINT / AUDIOBOOK

✔ **Synopsis/Things I liked:**

_____

_____

_____

_____

🚫 **Things I didn't like:**

_____

_____

_____

_____

✎ **Favorite quote(s):**

_____

_____

_____

_____

_____

_____

_____

TITLE: _____

GENRE: _____

SERIES: _____

AUTHOR: _____

PAGES: _____

STARTED: _____

FINISHED: _____

☆☆☆☆☆

FORMAT READ: EBOOK / PRINT / AUDIOBOOK

☑ **SYNOPSIS/THINGS I LIKED:**

_____
_____
_____
_____
_____

🚫 **THINGS I DIDN'T LIKE:**

_____
_____
_____
_____

📝 **FAVORITE QUOTE(S):**

_____
_____
_____
_____
_____
_____
_____

THE DUSTY DNFS (DID NOT FINISH)

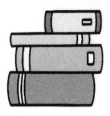

TITLE/PROGRESS:

COMMENTARY:

TITLE/PROGRESS:

COMMENTARY:

TITLE/PROGRESS:

COMMENTARY:

TITLE/PROGRESS:

COMMENTARY:

TITLE/PROGRESS:

COMMENTARY:

TITLE/PROGRESS:

COMMENTARY:

TITLE/PROGRESS:

COMMENTARY:

TITLE/PROGRESS:

COMMENTARY:

TITLE/PROGRESS:

COMMENTARY:

TITLE/PROGRESS:

COMMENTARY:

TITLE/PROGRESS:

COMMENTARY:

TITLE/PROGRESS:

COMMENTARY:

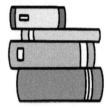

THE DUSTY
DNFS
(DID NOT FINISH)

TITLE/PROGRESS:

COMMENTARY:

TITLE/PROGRESS:

COMMENTARY:

TITLE/PROGRESS:

COMMENTARY:

TITLE/PROGRESS:

COMMENTARY:

TITLE/PROGRESS:

COMMENTARY:

TITLE/PROGRESS:

COMMENTARY:

TITLE/PROGRESS:

COMMENTARY:

TITLE/PROGRESS:

COMMENTARY:

TITLE/PROGRESS:

COMMENTARY:

TITLE/PROGRESS:

COMMENTARY:

TITLE/PROGRESS:

COMMENTARY:

TITLE/PROGRESS:

COMMENTARY:

THE DUSTY DNFS (DID NOT FINISH)

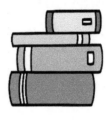

TITLE/PROGRESS:

COMMENTARY:

TITLE/PROGRESS:

COMMENTARY:

TITLE/PROGRESS:

COMMENTARY:

TITLE/PROGRESS:

COMMENTARY:

TITLE/PROGRESS:

COMMENTARY:

TITLE/PROGRESS:

COMMENTARY:

TITLE/PROGRESS:

COMMENTARY:

TITLE/PROGRESS:

COMMENTARY:

TITLE/PROGRESS:

COMMENTARY:

TITLE/PROGRESS:

COMMENTARY:

TITLE/PROGRESS:

COMMENTARY:

TITLE/PROGRESS:

COMMENTARY:

TITLE/PROGRESS:

COMMENTARY:

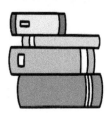

THE DUSTY DNFS (DID NOT FINISH)

TITLE/PROGRESS:

COMMENTARY:

TITLE/PROGRESS:

COMMENTARY:

TITLE/PROGRESS:

COMMENTARY:

TITLE/PROGRESS:

COMMENTARY:

TITLE/PROGRESS:

COMMENTARY:

TITLE/PROGRESS:

COMMENTARY:

TITLE/PROGRESS:

COMMENTARY:

TITLE/PROGRESS:

COMMENTARY:

TITLE/PROGRESS:

COMMENTARY:

TITLE/PROGRESS:

COMMENTARY:

TITLE/PROGRESS:

COMMENTARY:

TITLE/PROGRESS:

COMMENTARY:

The Dusty DNFs (Did Not Finish)

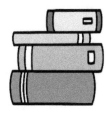

TITLE/PROGRESS:

COMMENTARY:

TITLE/PROGRESS:

COMMENTARY:

TITLE/PROGRESS:

COMMENTARY:

TITLE/PROGRESS:

COMMENTARY:

TITLE/PROGRESS:

COMMENTARY:

TITLE/PROGRESS:

COMMENTARY:

TITLE/PROGRESS:

COMMENTARY:

TITLE/PROGRESS:

COMMENTARY:

TITLE/PROGRESS:

COMMENTARY:

TITLE/PROGRESS:

COMMENTARY:

TITLE/PROGRESS:

COMMENTARY:

TITLE/PROGRESS:

COMMENTARY:

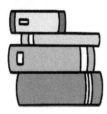

THE DUSTY
DNFS
(DID NOT FINISH)

TITLE/PROGRESS:

COMMENTARY:

TITLE/PROGRESS:

COMMENTARY:

TITLE/PROGRESS:

COMMENTARY:

TITLE/PROGRESS:

COMMENTARY:

TITLE/PROGRESS:

COMMENTARY:

TITLE/PROGRESS:

COMMENTARY:

TITLE/PROGRESS:

COMMENTARY:

TITLE/PROGRESS:

COMMENTARY:

TITLE/PROGRESS:

COMMENTARY:

TITLE/PROGRESS:

COMMENTARY:

TITLE/PROGRESS:

COMMENTARY:

TITLE/PROGRESS:

COMMENTARY:

TITLE/PROGRESS:

COMMENTARY:

About Me

Hundreds of books later...

Favorite Genres: _____

Favorite Books/Series: _____

Favorite Authors: _____

Favorite Book Characters: _____

Favorite Tropes: _____

Favorite Covers/Editions: _____

Favorite Places to Read: _____

Bookstore or Library? _____
Bookmark, Dog-ear, or Other? _____
Indie or Traditionally Published Books? _____
Ebook, Paperback, Hardback, or Audio? _____
Cracked or Preserved Spine? _____
My Reading Philosophy: _____
_____
_____
_____
_____

Refills & Book Recommendations

Pick up your next volume now!
Gems & Genres and *Titles & Treasures* are both premium book journals also offered by Painted Wings Publishing. They each accommodate entries for 250 books and have individual aesthetic touches.

THE SEEDER WARS TRILOGY

THE HEIR'S DUOLOGY

Seeder Wars is a Young Adult Contemporary Romantic Fantasy series featuring unique magic, botanical beings, spies, & assassins. The series starts with a central trilogy and expands to a spin-off duology (& more on the way!)

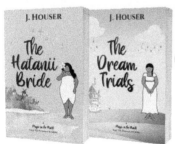

Magic in the Match is a series of standalone Adult Fairy Tale Sweet Romances.

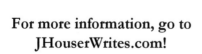

Magic in the Match Fairy Tale Romances

For more information, go to
JHouserWrites.com!

Lightning Source UK Ltd.
Milton Keynes UK
UKHW020609190223
417146UK00004B/31/J

9 781957 334059